CHRISTIANITY
THE RENEWAL
OF NATURE

Creation, climate change and
human responsibility

Edited by
SEBASTIAN C. H. KIM
and
JONATHAN DRAPER

First published in Great Britain in 2011

Society for Promoting Christian Knowledge
36 Causton Street
London SW1P 4ST
www.spckpublishing.co.uk

British Library Cataloguing-in-Publication Data
A catalogue record for this book is available from the British Library

ISBN 978–0–281–06331–4

Typeset by Graphicraft Ltd, Hong Kong
First printed in Great Britain by Ashford Colour Press
Subsequently digitally printed in Great Britain

Produced on paper from sustainable forests

Contents

Acknowledgements

The Ebor Lectures were conceived as a response to the growing need for theology to interact with public issues of contemporary society; they aim to promote public conversation and to contribute to the formation of personal decisions and collective policy-making in the economic, political and social spheres. This ongoing series of lectures is organized by York Minster (represented by the Revd Canon Dr Jonathan Draper), York St John University (Professor Sebastian Kim), York Institute for Community Theology (the Revd Richard Andrew), the Order of Carmelites (Fr Tony Lester) and the Churches Regional Commission (the Revd Liz Carnelley). Suzanne Parkes, coordinator of the Ebor Lectures, completes the committee. A relevant theme is chosen each year, and the lectures are delivered alternately at York Minster and York St John University between September and June. The combined annual lectures are published in book form to make them available to a wider audience. Our desire is to use these lectures as an instrument to promote serious thinking and reflection on contemporary issues from the perspective of faith. The lectures relate faith to public concerns including politics, economics, contemporary culture, religion and spirituality, society and globalization. They are also an ecumenical project which seeks to exchange insights between academic and religious traditions, and to build bridges between churches and other faith groups.

The editors, together with the members of the Ebor Lectures committee, wish to acknowledge those who have contributed to the Ebor Lecture series: Professor David Fleming; Professor David Maughan-Brown and the Dean, Deputy Dean and staff of the Faculty of Education and Theology at York St John University; the Very Revd Keith Jones, the chapter and staff of York Minster; the Revd Stephen Burgess of the Methodist Church; and Fr Wilfrid McGreal of the Order of Carmelites. The conduct of the lectures was carried out by Suzanne Parkes, Ebor Lectures coordinator, whose efforts have made the series successful, and others who have helped in various ways. In particular, we wish to acknowledge Alex Carberry of York Minster and Sian Henderson of York

Institute for Community Theology for their contributions. For the publication of the series, we wish to express our appreciation to Rebecca Mulhearn and Philip Law of SPCK for their insightful suggestions.

Contributors

Jonathan Draper is Canon Theologian of York Minster. Previously he was Vicar of Putney in south-west London, taught systematic theology at Ripon College Cuddesdon and was a member of the Faculty of Theology at Oxford University. He is the author of *To Love and Serve* (London: SPCK, 2003). He is married with three children.

Tim Gorringe is St Luke's Professor of Theological Studies at the University of Exeter. He worked in parishes for six years before going to south India to teach theology at the Tamil Nadu Theological Seminary, where he worked for seven years. After his return to Britain he was for nine years Chaplain, Fellow and Tutor in Theology at St John's College, Oxford. In 1995 he became Reader in Contextual Theology at the University of St Andrews. His academic interests focus on the interrelation between theology, social science, art and politics. Aside from theology he is a bee-keeper, poultry-keeper, theatre-goer, home winemaker, political activist and poetry lover, and a member of the Iona Community.

Mary Grey is an ecofeminist liberation theologian, until recently D. J. James Professor of Pastoral Theology at the University of Wales, Lampeter, and formerly Professor of Contemporary Theology at the University of Southampton, based at La Sainte Union (1993–7). Before that she was Professor of Feminism and Christianity at the Catholic University of Nijmegen, the Netherlands. She is now Professorial Research Fellow at St Mary's University College, Twickenham, London. Her recent writing includes: *Introducing Feminist Images of God* (London: Continuum, 2001), *Sacred Longings: Ecofeminist Theology and Globalisation* (London: SCM, 2003; Philadelphia: Fortress, 2004), *The Unheard Scream: The Struggles of Dalit Women in India* (New Delhi: ISPCK, 2004) and *Pursuing the Dream: A Jewish–Christian Conversation*, with Rabbi Dan Cohn-Sherbok (London: Darton, Longman & Todd, 2005). For ten years she was editor of the journal *Ecotheology*.

Sebastian Kim is Professor of Theology and Public Life in the Faculty of Education and Theology of York St John University. A Fellow of the Royal Asiatic Society, he is the author of *In Search of Identity: Debates on Religious Conversion in India* (Oxford: Oxford University Press, 2003) and co-author of *Christianity as a World Religion* (London: Continuum, 2008). He was formerly Director of the Christianity in Asia Project and taught World Christianity at the Faculty of Divinity of the University of Cambridge. He is founding and current editor of the *International Journal of Public Theology*.

Michael Northcott is Professor of Ethics in the School of Divinity in the University of Edinburgh. He formerly served as a parish priest in Manchester, and as a lecturer in the Seminari Theologi Malaysia in Kuala Lumpur. His research interests are at the interface between theology and the social and natural sciences and his books include *The Environment and Christian Ethics* (Cambridge: Cambridge University Press, 1996), *A Moral Climate: The Ethics of Global Warming* (London: Darton, Longman & Todd, 2007), *Cuttle Fish, Clones and Cluster Bombs* (London: Darton, Longman & Todd, 2010) and, with R. J. Berry, *Theology After Darwin* (Carlisle: Paternoster, 2009) and, with Kyle Vanhoutan, *Dominion and Diversity* (Eugene, OR: Wipf and Stock, 2010). He speaks and writes extensively beyond the academy to churches and other organizations and, in the media, is a trustee of the fair-trade organization Traidcraft, and is on the board of the climate change charity Operation Noah. He also has a smallholding and grows much of his own food.

Clive Pearson is Associate Professor; Associate Director of the Centre for Public and Contextual Theologies; Principal of United Theological College, Sydney; and Head of the School of Theology, Charles Sturt University, Australia. He is currently completing a book on the nature and purpose of a public theology viewed from the perspective of Australia and New Zealand.

Martin Redfern is a senior producer in the BBC Radio Science Unit where he has worked for most of the last 25 years. Before that he graduated in geology from University College London, joining the BBC as a studio manager. He has spent time as a science producer for BBC TV and as science news editor for the BBC World Service. Most of his work now is on science feature programmes for Radio 4 and the World Service, for which he has won many awards, including three from the Association of British Science Writers. In 2005 he was awarded a Templeton Cambridge Journalism Fellowship in Science and Religion and he is an adviser to that scheme. He is also a director of the Scientific and Medical Network. He spent a month in Antarctica in February 2008 reporting on climate change and he has completed a 30-part series on the history of cosmology.

John Sauven is Executive Director of Greenpeace UK, a position he has held since September 2007. Prior to this he was the director responsible for Greenpeace Communications and for working on solutions with business, a role which allowed him to coordinate an international campaign which secured a moratorium on further destruction of the Amazon by soya producers. His work has brought together a huge alliance of US and European multinationals involved in the soya production, commodity trading and food retailing sectors, and of their Brazilian counterparts. Thanks to the alliance, this has proved to be one of Greenpeace's most successful campaigns, providing both climate and biodiversity protection across wide areas of the world's largest intact rainforests.

Clare Short was Secretary of State for International Development from 1997 to May 2003. She entered the House of Commons in 1983 as the Member of Parliament for Birmingham Ladywood, the area where she was born and grew up, and held the constituency until her retirement in 2010. Since 2003 she has been a member of the International Advisory Board for the Geneva Centre for the Democratic Control of Armed Forces (GDAF) and in 2004 she became an Associate of the Oxford Research Group. Since 2006, Short has been a member of the Policy Advisory Board of Cities Alliance, an alliance of the World Bank, UN–HABITAT, local government and development partners committed to meeting the UN target to develop cities without slums. She is the author of *An Honourable Deception? New Labour, Iraq, and the Misuse of Power* (London: Free Press, 2004), which was awarded the title of Political Book of the Year by Channel 4.

Rowan Williams has been the 104th Archbishop of Canterbury since December 2002. In 1983 he was appointed as a lecturer in Divinity in the University of Cambridge, and the following year became Dean and Chaplain of Clare College. In 1986 he returned to Oxford, where he had completed his D.Phil., as Lady Margaret Professor of Divinity and Canon of Christ Church; he was awarded the degree of Doctor of Divinity in 1989, and became a Fellow of the British Academy in 1990. In 1991 Williams accepted election and consecration as Bishop of Monmouth, a diocese on the Welsh borders, and in 1999 he was elected Archbishop of Wales. Williams is acknowledged internationally as an outstanding theological writer, scholar and teacher. He has written extensively across a very wide range of related fields of professional study – philosophy, theology, spirituality and religious aesthetics.

Introduction

SEBASTIAN C. H. KIM

'When you send your Spirit, they are created, and you renew the face
of the earth.'

(Psalm 104.30, NIV)

The reality of climate change, and the challenges it presents to sustainable living, are perhaps the key issues facing humanity at present. The
developing ecological crisis raises profound questions for theology,
religious traditions, politics and economics. Governments, various
NGOs and religious communities have been engaging with these
issues and are actively involved in shaping both theoretical and
practical responses. In particular, in recent years the Christian churches
have made conscious attempts to deal with the problem in three
ways: Christian leaders are attempting to make the Church aware of
its responsibility in the issue; Christian groups and organizations are
providing practical tools for action; and theologians are reshaping
our understanding of theology in relation to ecological crisis.

First, as a collective effort of Christian churches, the World Council
of Churches (WCC) initiated the 'Justice, Peace and the Integrity of
Creation' programme (now 'Justice, Diakonia and Responsibility for
Creation'). In particular, the Conference on World Mission and
Evangelism, meeting at San Antonio in 1989, reaffirmed the stewardship of human beings over God's creation and the importance of
seeking justice in the sharing of land. Human beings have a ministry
to be 'guardians of nature', as the San Antonio report affirms: 'Because
the earth is the Lord's, the responsibility of the church towards the
earth is a crucial part of the church's ministry.' The conference emphasized God's mandate to human beings to 'till it [the earth] and keep
it' (Gen. 2.15) rather than 'to subdue it; and have dominion over' it
(Gen. 1.28). 'Justice, peace and the integrity of creation' has been a
dominant theme for the ecumenical tradition for a number of years
and has made a significant impact on the life of the churches. To
bring about justice, human beings need to recover the role in creation
given to them by God, which means reaffirming God's creative activity

in and through ourselves as human beings. This is characterized as 'stewardship' and needs to be reinforced in the theology and ministry of the Church.[1] In the lead-up to the United Nations Conference on Climate Change in Copenhagen, which took place on 7–18 December 2009, the WCC mobilized the 'Countdown to Copenhagen'. It collected more than half a million signatures and conducted a bell-ringing and prayer campaign on 13 December. In a letter to the president of the conference, it stated that 'it will be a subject of justice and wisdom towards our planet and the entire good creation of God, to see the same promptness from the global community in responding to the climate change crisis, as the way in which it dealt with the financial and economic crisis', and concluded, 'Do not be afraid! Act now!'[2]

From the Catholic Church, the Vatican's Council for Justice and Peace hosted the Pontifical Council on Climate Change and Development in April 2007, inviting prominent scientists, environment ministers and leaders of various religions from 20 different countries. The main issue discussed at the conference was the balance between environmental concern for nature and the developmental needs of people. The participants called for the Vatican to focus on the ethical and moral challenges posed by climate change.[3] In the recent Pontifical Encyclical of Pope Benedict XVI, *Caritas in Veritate* ('Charity in Truth', 29 June 2009), the Catholic leadership has expressed its view on the issue of the environment. The encyclical emphasizes that the environment is God's gift to everyone, but that the Church has a particular responsibility to use it for the care of the poor. It also states that nature reflects the Creator and his love for humanity, but cautions against either seeing nature as something more important than human beings or treating it as the object of exploitation. It calls for 'renewed solidarity' to share natural resources between the rich and the poor and for 'responsible stewardship over nature', and insists that the Church in particular has this responsibility in the public sphere. The encyclical also emphasizes the importance of human ecology, in which our attitudes to other human beings and to nature are interconnected, and that the 'decisive issue is the overall moral tenor of society'.[4]

Meanwhile, among evangelicals, a significant step towards dealing with climate change was the statement made by 280 American evangelical leaders in January 2006 and entitled 'Climate Change: An

Evangelical Call to Action'. The signatories recognized the impact of climate change both on the poor and vulnerable and on future generations, and affirmed four principles: the reality of human-induced climate change; the devastating consequences of climate change for the poor; the responsibility of Christians on the basis of moral convictions; and the urgency of immediate action. On this basis, they called for Christians to 'make personal changes and rally action', and for policy-makers 'to make wise and moral choices' to protect God's world and its people.[5]

Second, it is very encouraging to see various Christian NGOs specifically addressing the issue of climate change. A Rocha (the name is derived from a Portuguese word meaning a rock) is among the most active international Christian groups working for the environment. Its activities are founded on commitments which include: faith in God who entrusts the world to the care of human society; research and education for conservation and restoration of the natural world; and working with local communities and in partnership with wider communities and individuals. A Rocha provides resources such as ideas for sermons, service outlines, material for children and young people, and group studies. Similarly, Operation Noah, Christian Ecology Link, Christian Aid, CAFOD, Tearfund, the European Christian Environment Network, and the Environment and Climate Change theme within Churches Together in Britain and Ireland provide web resources, printed materials, news updates and networking among those who are concerned. They also conduct regular conferences and workshops designed to encourage local congregations to get involved in promoting the cause. An increasing number of special projects are taking place within different church denominations and other faith organizations, such as the Islamic Foundation for Ecology and Environmental Sciences, Ecological Buddhism and The Big Green Jewish Website.[6] The strength of these movements is their practical suggestions for local religious communities and individuals to do whatever they can in their own situation, and these local initiatives are increasingly gaining support from the general public.

Third, alongside the growing practical concern with ecological issues, there have been theological discussions – led by Michael Northcott, Celia Deane-Drummond and David Hallman, among others – on such issues, providing resources and insights that contribute to the development of what is commonly called 'eco-theology'. Eco-theology is concerned with 'the environment and humanity's relationship with the natural world' and seeks to 'uncover the theological basis for a proper relationship between God, humanity and the cosmos'.[7] Michael Northcott insists that the environmental crisis requires a 'radical change to the predominant direction of human behaviour' rather than new technology and regulations. Although the latter are important, he is convinced that the issue is an ethical one, which demands 'recovery of a spiritual, moral and cosmological awareness of our place in the natural order', and that ethical teaching from religious traditions could contribute in a significant way to dealing with the problem. He sees a purely material and scientific reading of environmental issues as missing the point that redemption requires moral and spiritual conversion as well.[8] Northcott emphasizes that the Hebrew Bible and the Christian doctrine of natural law offer significant insights into God's created order, an account of the interaction between human beings and the ecological order, and relations between these and God. A renewed examination of the Sabbath of the land and the *shalom* of the earth will show us our duty to preserve God's created order, since we are part and parcel of the whole system rather than above it.[9] In her comprehensive study on eco-theology, Deane-Drummond discusses various theological attempts to relate ecology and theology, arguing that ecology is the 'universal vocation' for Christians and should be at the heart of Christian faith and practice. She insists on the importance of the biblical wisdom traditions of the Sabbath, which she regards as the ethos for eco-theology – 'living from the Sabbath is a reminder to the human community to live according to covenant responsibility' – and also helps us to approach nature with respect and humility.[10]

There have been an increasing number of publications on the Church's response to the ecological crisis, and ecology has now become an important item on the agenda of theology. Eco-theology has challenged traditional theologies and has not only given the Church and its ministry new and fresh insights but has also led to a re-examination of Scripture and the understanding of human beings and nature. Eco-theology has emerged as theologians have wrestled with several challenges. These include, first, the criticism of traditional theologies, which are accused of being anthropocentric (human centred) and androcentric (man – not woman – centred). As such they are accused of complicity in colonialism, environmental destruction and the oppression of women. This is seen as largely due to the understanding of the creation narrative (especially Gen. 1.28) as affirming human – particularly male – domination over other beings. Second is the failure of traditional theologies to respond to the problems of the ecosystem, and their silence in the face of development and technology models which have been the main contributing factors to the present crisis. Third is the encounter with the people and philosophies of other religious traditions. Christian theologians have found deep insight among people of other faiths concerning the relationship between humankind and nature. This has brought to the fore the question of how and to what extent Christian theology can learn from the more integrated systems of other religions and indigenous spiritualities.

As I have briefly mentioned above, churches, along with other religious communities, have made considerable progress in approaching the current ecological crisis and are actively participating in addressing the issues in various ways. As a part of these endeavours, this volume has brought church leaders, theologians, scientists, media personnel, activists and politicians together to examine the roots and causes of this global emergency from a variety of perspectives and to look at the implications of the crisis for future sustainable living on the planet. The strength of this volume is that the contributors not only offer various perspectives from their own expertise, each making distinctive contributions to the issue, but also interact with each other's insights, demonstrating the interdisciplinary nature of the problem. They call for religious communities to take the issue seriously and get involved in dealing with the problem through critical enquiry, open debate and practical action.

Rowan Williams starts by exploring God's glory and sovereignty over the relationship of human beings with nature. Showing that the language of redemption in Scripture often applies both to people and nature, and that both are in the hand of God, he further asserts that our task is to seek ways to preserve and nourish an integral approach to both human beings and their environment. For this, a proper use of intelligence is vital for dealing with the problem: God has given us the ability to change our situation, but more significantly, vision can renew intelligence, and faith can play a significant role in this process. Williams strongly contests the idea that God might somehow protect us from failure in our duty to care for the environment, and insists that such a belief is unchristian and unbiblical. For him, according to Psalm 104, through the breathing of God (the sending of his Spirit) on creation, the face of the earth is renewed, which is the 'movement that carries our love and intelligence in the same direction, so that we can properly make answer for, be responsible for, our world'.

Tim Gorringe discusses the book of Revelation (especially chapter 8) in order to bring to bear relevant insights on climate change from a theological perspective. He identifies the problem of a development agenda that fails properly to consider the consequences, an agenda which has brought about the current crisis and which costs the whole inhabited earth. This, he believes, is largely an outcome of the distorted modern world view of technology and the market economy. After extensive study, Gorringe suggests that the text is not meant to predict the end of the world, but rather is imagining the 'destruction of destructive powers'. This destruction is what he sees as God's liberative judgement, which opens hope for the earth and humankind. He further insists that the texts provide hope based on faith and not merely on optimism, and that they also call for repentance and action in more concrete and practical ways.

Similarly, Mary Grey expounds Scripture to deal with the topic; in this case Luke's Gospel. She believes the Scriptures offer resources for change and reminds us of the sacred duty God has entrusted in human beings towards the environment. She identifies Luke's Gospel as providing insights for the discussion of climate change, and expands the passages from a liberation-theological perspective. Discussing examples of the effects of climate change on the lives of people in Rajasthan, north-west India, and in Palestine, particularly with regard to the problem of the shortage of water and land for cultivation, she suggests some lessons drawn from the study: the urgency of the matter, the call for perseverance and prayer, and the need for a sacrificial lifestyle, an attitude of hospitality and welcome, wisdom to meet the challenge, and the Spirit for wisdom and creativity. She concludes that Luke demonstrates the 'wisdom of creation' to 'inspire and guide us through this crisis into God's redeemed future for *all* created life'.

From the perspective of a journalist, Martin Redfern presents, using his wealth of experience and insight, some of the past and current debates relating to climate change. He asserts that climate change is 'the defining challenge' of the twenty-first century, and that it deter-mines the quality of life and the very survival of future generations. He discusses some of the difficulties of the scientific community in establishing the reality of climate change and in convincing politicians to take action, and gives his own account of the effects of climate change in Antarctica to make clear his point that global warming is a reality which is supported by overwhelming scientific evidence. Redfern sharply criticizes tendencies towards reductionism among scientists and towards dualism among religious people, and calls for an integral approach to the problem by different members of soci-ety. He concludes with a quotation from a meditation by Shantanand Saraswati.

John Sauven, a Greenpeace activist, challenges readers about the urgency of climate change and calls for immediate action from all. Employing various statistics and scientific discoveries, he argues that climate change is a far greater problem for us than the economic crisis, particularly in view of its urgency and its effect on future generations. Sauven particularly criticizes governments that spend huge sums building up weapons systems, people's habitual consump-tion of natural resources, and the obsession with development, growth and progress at the cost of natural resources. In order to achieve environmental sustainability, he suggests, there should be more innov-ation to maximize production at the same time as minimizing the use of natural resources. He urges us to develop a culture of habits which lead to less consumption and stronger global institutions to deal with ecological issues. He insists that the issue of climate change is neither a scientific nor an economic one but a 'human challenge', and he presents some practical guidelines, including the need to define the levels of consumption and emissions which are sustainable; to avoid using short-lived disposable goods; to develop a new model of ownership to be responsible for sustainable development; and to consider the poor as a priority concern.

Both Michael Northcott and Clive Pearson discuss the public role of the Church in tackling the issue and provide some practical sug-gestions. Northcott argues that the Kyoto Protocol and the United Nations Framework Convention on Climate Change have failed, due to the employment of neoliberal market techniques for the manage-ment of emissions reduction. He suggests that the Church's task is to offer a theological critique of this approach and to promote a spiritual theology of cooperative action for the common good. Pearson, on the other hand, propounds his thesis that active engagement with ecological issues lies at the heart of doing theology in the public sphere. To do this, he discusses the ideas put forward by various contemporary theologians, especially John de Gruchy, Michael Northcott and Robert Schreiter, and also examines the cases of Tuvalu in the Pacific in its problem of rising sea level and Australia in its government's responses to the Kyoto Protocol.

In the final chapter, Clare Short presents insights drawn from her rich experience in politics. She sees the present context as decadent, and calls for the building of a 'new, more moral, sustainable and generous civilization'. For that we need to recapture 'hope and energy in order to create the world of justice and peace'. She gives examples from many parts of the globe and suggests some practical ways of improving the current 'unequal and divided' world. Short particularly emphasizes the importance of local community initiatives, and the urgency and scale of the human action needed to respond to the enormous problem we face in contemporary society. The format of this chapter follows a different pattern from the others, including questions and answers.

Responding to the ecological challenge is part and parcel of the role of the Church, which has a responsibility to face this overwhelming crisis. And as it carries out its responsibility towards the creation as part of its ministry, the Church should establish sound theological perspectives on the issue, formulate practical steps for church members, and actually engage in changing the situation. This volume aims to support the above endeavour of the Church, together with the wider community, for the 'renewal of nature', or as the psalmist expressed it, 'renewing the face of the earth'.

1

Renewing the face of the earth: Human responsibility and the environment

ROWAN WILLIAMS

Some modern philosophers have spoken about the human face as the most potent sign of what it is that we can't master or exhaust in the life of a human other – a sign of the claim upon us of the other, of the depths we can't sound but must respect. And while it is of course so ancient a metaphor to talk about the 'face' of the earth that we barely notice any longer that it *is* a metaphor, it does no harm to let some of these associations find their way into our thinking; because such associations resonate so strongly with a fundamental biblical insight into the nature of our relationship with the world we inhabit.

'The earth is the LORD's', says the twenty-fourth psalm. In its context, this is primarily an assertion of God's glory and overall sovereignty. And it affirms a relation between God and the world that is independent of what we as human beings think about the world or do to the world. The world is in the hands of another. The earth we inhabit is more than we can get hold of in any one moment or even in the sum total of all the moments we spend with it. Its destiny is not bound only to human destiny, its story is not exhausted by the history of our particular culture or technology, or even by the history of the entire human race. We can't as humans oblige the environment to follow our agenda in all things, however much we can bend certain natural forces to our will; we can't control the weather system or the succession of the seasons. The world turns, and the tides move at the drawing of the moon. Human force is incapable of changing any of this. What is before me is a network of relations and interconnections in which the relation to *me*, or even to us collectively as human beings, is very far from the whole story. I may ignore this, but only at the cost of disaster. And it would be dangerously illusory to imagine that this material environment will adjust itself at all costs so as to maintain our relationship to it. If it is more than us and our relation with it, it can survive us; we are dispensable. But the earth remains the Lord's.

And this language is used still more pointedly in a passage like Leviticus 25.23: we are foreign and temporary tenants on a soil that belongs to the Lord. We can never *possess* the land in which we live, so as to do what we like with it. In a brilliant recent monograph, the American Old Testament scholar Ellen Davis points out that the twenty-fifth chapter of Leviticus is in fact a sustained argument about enslavement and alienation in a number of interconnected contexts. The people and the land alike belong to God – so that 'ownership' of a person within God's chosen community is anomalous in a similar way to ownership of the land. When the Israelite loses family property, he must live alongside members of his family as if he were a resident alien (25.35); but the reader is reminded that in relation to God, the entire community, settled by God of his own gratuitous gift in the land of Canaan, has the same status of resident aliens. And when there is no alternative for the impoverished person but to be sold into slavery, an Israelite buying such a slave must treat him as a hired servant; if the purchaser is not an Israelite, there is an urgent obligation on the family to see that the person is redeemed. Davis points out that the obligation to redeem the enslaved Israelite is connected by way of several verbal echoes with the obligation defined earlier of redeeming, buying back, family land alienated as a result of poverty (vv. 24–28). The language of redemption applies both to the land and to the people; both are in God's hands, and thus the people called to imitate the holiness of God will be seeking to save both persons and property from being alienated for ever from their primary and defining relation to the God of the Exodus.[1]

A primary and defining relation: this is the core of a biblical ethic of responsibility for the environment. To understand that we and our environment are alike in the hands of God, so that neither can be possessed absolutely, is to see that the mysteriousness of the interior life of another person and the uncontrollable difference and resistance of the material world are connected. Both demand that we do not regard relationships centred upon *us*, upon our individual or group agendas, as the determining factor in how we approach persons or things. If, as this whole section of Leviticus assumes, God's people are called to reflect what God is like, to make God's holiness visible, then just or good action is action which reflects God's purpose of *liberating* persons and environment from possession and the exploitation that comes from it – liberating them in order that their 'primary and defining relation' may be realized. Just action, towards people and environment, is letting created reality, both human and non-human, stand before God unhindered by attempts to control and dominate.

Responsibility for creation

It is a rather different reading of the biblical tradition from that often (lazily) assumed to be the orthodoxy of Judaeo-Christian belief. We hear regularly that this tradition authorizes the exploitation of the earth through the language in Genesis about 'having dominion' over the non-human creation. As has been argued elsewhere, this is a very clumsy reading of what Genesis actually says; but set alongside the Levitical code and (as Ellen Davis argues) many other aspects of the theology of Jewish Scripture, the malign interpretation that has latterly been taken for granted by critics of Judaism and Christianity appears profoundly mistaken. But what remains to be teased out is more about the nature of the human calling to further the 'redemption' of persons and world. If liberating action is allowing things and persons to stand before God free from claims to possession, is the responsibility of human agents only to stand back and let natural processes unfold?

In Genesis, humanity is given the task of 'cultivating' the garden of Eden: we are not left simply to observe or stand back, but are endowed with the responsibility to preserve and direct the powers of nature. In this process, we become more fully and joyfully who and what we are – as St Augustine memorably says, commenting on this passage: there is a joy, he says, in the 'experiencing of the powers of nature'. Our own fulfilment is bound up with the work of conserving and focusing those powers, and the exercise of this work is meant to be one of the things that holds us in Paradise and makes it possible to resist temptation. The implication is that an attitude to work which regards the powers of nature as simply a threat to be overcome is best seen as an effect of the Fall, a sign of alienation. And, as the monastic scholar Aelred Squire points out, this insight of Augustine, quoted by Thomas Aquinas, is echoed by Aquinas himself in another passage where he describes humanity as having a share in the working of divine Providence because it has the task of using its reasoning powers to *provide* for self and others (*aliis*, which can mean both persons and things).[2] In other words, the human task is to draw out potential treasures in the powers of nature and so to realize the convergent process of humanity and nature discovering in collaboration what they can become. The 'redemption' of people and material life in general is not a matter of resigning from the business of labour and of transformation – as if we could – but the search for a form of action that will preserve and nourish an interconnected development of humanity and its environment. In some contexts, this will be the deliberate *protection* of the environment from harm: in a world where exploitative and aggressive behaviour is commonplace, one of the 'providential' tasks of human beings must be to limit damage and to secure space for the natural order to exist unharmed. In others, the question is rather how to use the natural order for the sake of human nourishment and security without pillaging its resources and so damaging its inner mechanisms for self-healing or self-correction. In both, the fundamental requirement is to discern enough of what the processes of nature truly are to be able to engage intelligently with them.

All of this suggests some definitions of what unintelligent and ungodly relation with the environment looks like. It is partial: that is, it refuses to see or understand that what can be grasped about natural processes is likely to be only one dimension of interrelations far more complex than we can gauge. It focuses on aspects of the environment that can be comparatively easily manipulated for human advantage and ignores inconvenient questions about what less obvious connections are being violated. It is indifferent, for example, to the way in which biodiversity is part of the self-balancing system of the world we inhabit. It is impatient: it seeks returns on labour that are prompt and low cost, without consideration of long-term effects. It avoids or denies the basic truth that the environment as a material system is finite and cannot indefinitely regenerate itself in ways that will simply fulfil human needs or wants. And when such unintelligent and ungodly relation prevails, the risks should be obvious. We discover too late that we have turned a blind eye to the extinction

4

of a species that is essential to the balance of life in a particular context. Or we discover too late that the importation of a foreign life-form, animal or vegetable, has upset local ecosystems, damaging soil or neighbouring life-forms. We discover that we have come near the end of supplies – of fossil fuels for example – on which we have built immense structures of routine expectation. Increasingly, we have to face the possibility not only of the now familiar problems of climate change, bad enough as these are, but of a whole range of 'doomsday' prospects. Martin Rees's 2003 book *Our Final Century* outlined some of these, noting also that the technology which in the hands of benign agents is assumed to be working for the good of humanity is the same technology which, universally available on the internet, can enable 'bio-terror', the threat to release pathogens against a population.[3] This feels like an ultimate reversal of the relation between humanity and environment envisaged in the religious vision – the material world's processes deliberately harnessed to bring about domination by violence; though, when you think about it, it is only a projection of the existing history of military technology.

A. S. Byatt's novel *The Biographer's Tale* tells the story – or rather a set of interconnected stories – of a writer engaging with the literary remains of a diverse collection of people, including Linnaeus, the great Swedish botanist.[4] Late in the book (pp. 243–4), Fulla, a Swedish entomologist, holds forth to the narrator and his friends about the varieties of devastation the world faces because of our ignorance of insect life, specifically the life of bees:

> She told fearful tales of possible lurches in the population of pollinators (including those of the crops we depend on for our own lives). Tales of the destruction of the habitats by humans, and of benign and necessary insects, birds, bats and other creatures, by crop-spraying and road-building . . . Of the need to find other (often better) pollinators, in a world where they are being extinguished swiftly and silently. Of the fact that there are only thirty-nine qualified bee taxonomists in the world, whose average age is sixty . . . Of population problems, and feeding the world, and sesbania, a leguminous crop which could both hold back desertification, because it binds soil, and feed the starving, but for the fact that no one has studied its pollinators or their abundance or deficiency, or their habits, in sufficient detail.

It is a potent catalogue of unintelligence.

Earlier in the book (p. 205), Fulla has said that 'We are an animal that needs to use its intelligence to mitigate the effects of its intelligence on the other creatures' – a notable definition in the contemporary context of what the Levitical call to redemption might mean. We cannot *but* use our intelligence in our world, and we are bound to use it, as Fulla's examples suggest, to supply need, to avoid famine and suffering. If the Christian vision outlined by Aquinas is truthful, intelligence is an aspect of sharing in God's Providence and so it is committed to providing for others. But God's Providence does not promote the good only of one sector of creation; and so we have to use our intelligence to seek the good of the whole system of which we are a part. The limits of our creative manipulation of what is put before us in our environment are not instantly self-evident, of course; but what is coming into focus is the level of risk involved if we never ask such a question, if we collude with a social and economic order that apparently takes the possibility of unlimited advance in material prosperity for granted, and systematically ignores the big picture of global interconnectedness (in economics or in ecology).

Ecological questions are increasingly being defined as issues of justice; climate change has been characterized as a matter of justice both to those who now have no part in decision-making at the global level yet bear the heaviest burdens as a consequence of the irresponsibility of wealthier nations, and to those who will succeed us on this planet – justice to our children and grandchildren (this is spelled out clearly in Paula Clifford's new book, *Angels with Trumpets: The Church in a Time of Global Warming*).[5] So the major issue we need to keep in view is how much injustice is let loose by any given set of economic or manufacturing practices. We can't easily set out a straightforward code that will tell us precisely when and where we step across the line into the unintelligence and ungodliness I have sketched. But we can at least see that the question is asked, and asked on the basis of a clear recognition that there is no way of manipulating our environment that is without cost or consequence – and thus also of a recognition that we are inextricably bound up with the destiny of our world. There is no guarantee that the world we live in will 'tolerate' us indefinitely if we prove ourselves unable to live within its constraints.

Is this – as some would claim – a failure to trust God, who has promised faithfulness to what he has made? I think that to suggest that God might intervene to protect us from the corporate folly of our practices is as unchristian and unbiblical as to suggest that he protects us from the results of our individual folly or sin. This is not a creation in which there are no real risks: our faith has always held that the inexhaustible love of God cannot compel justice or virtue; we are capable of doing immeasurable damage to ourselves as individuals, and it seems clear that we have the same terrible freedom as a human race. God's faithfulness stands, assuring us that even in the most appalling disaster love will not let us go; but it will not be a safety net that guarantees a happy ending in this world. Any religious language that implies this is making a nonsense of the prophetic tradition of the Old Testament and the urgency of the preaching of Jesus.

But to say this is also to be reminded of the fact that intelligence *is* given to us; we are capable of changing our situation – and, as A. S. Byatt's character puts it, using our intelligence to limit the ruinous effects of our intelligence. If we can change things so appallingly for the worse, it is possible to change them for the better also. But, in Christian terms, this needs a radical change of heart, a conversion; it needs another kind of 'redemption', which frees us from the trap of an egotism that obscures judgement. Intelligence in regard to the big picture of our world is no neutral thing, no simple natural capacity of reasoning; it needs grace to escape from the distortions of pride and acquisitiveness. One of the things we as Christians ought to be saying in the context of the ecological debate is that human reasoning in its proper and fullest sense requires an awareness of our participation in the material processes of the world and thus a sense of its own involvement in what it cannot finally master. Being rational is not a wholly detached capacity, examining the phenomena of the world from a distance, but a set of skills for finding our way around in the physical world.

An intelligent response to environmental crisis

The ecological crisis challenges us to be reasonable. Put like that, it sounds banal; but given the level of irrationality around the question, it is well worth saying, especially if we are clear about the roots of reasoning in these 'skills' of negotiating the world of material objects. I don't intend to discuss in detail the rhetoric of those who deny the reality of climate change, except to say that rhetoric (as King Canute demonstrated) does not turn back rising waters. If you live in Bangladesh or Tuvalu, scepticism about global warming is precisely the opposite of reasonable: 'negotiating' this environment means recognizing the fact of rising sea levels; and understanding what is happening necessarily involves recognizing how rising temperatures affect sea levels. It is possible to argue about the exact degree to which human intervention is responsible for these phenomena (though it would be a quite remarkable coincidence if massively increased levels of carbon emissions merely *happened* to accompany a routine cyclical change in global temperatures, given the obvious explanatory force of the presence of these emissions), but it is not possible rationally to deny what the inhabitants of low-lying territories in the world routinely face as the most imminent threat to their lives and livelihoods.

And what the perspective of faith – in particular of Christian faith – brings to this discussion is the insight that we are not and don't have to be God. For us to be reasonable and free and responsible is for us to live in awareness of our limits and dependence. It is no lessening of our dignity as humans, let alone our rationality and liberty as humans, if we exercise these 'godlike' gifts in the context of bodies that are fragile and mortal and a world that we do not completely control. I suggested recently that this current financial crisis had more to do with pride than with greed – understanding pride as the attempt to forget or obliterate our sense of living within limits and lacking total control. Intelligent life in these circumstances is not the triumphant imposition of human will upon a defeated natural order, but the reasoned discovery of how we live in such a way as not to destroy a balance in the natural order which we sense rather than fully grasp. It is to turn away from denial – from all those denials of our finite condition that were summed up many years since in a famous book by Ernst Becker, *The Denial of Death*, in which he identified the basic pathology of the human mind as the fantasy of being 'self-created'.[6]

Such denial is not properly understood as deliberate refusal of the truth; it is in large part a consequence of the perceived complexity of the global situation, a complexity that produces both paralysis and a stubborn adherence to failed or outdated paradigms. Jonathon Porritt, in his magisterial work *Capitalism as If the World Matters*, ascribes the 'continuing, utterly perverse denial on the part of politicians' to a failure to grasp that much of the very complexity which makes people stick to policies they think they understand is itself the result of 'the dominant paradigm of progress through exponential economic growth'.[7] Unfortunately, he goes on, too few politicians who *have* grasped the issue have worked out carefully enough what 'transitional strategies' would be possible for the reimagining of a broadly capitalist practice (i.e. an economic practice that values risk and innovation and enables increased collective wealth through trade) that was not systematically disastrous for the environment. His book attempts to offer some starting points for such work – noting, soberly, that denial of a different kind afflicts many green movements, whose campaigning style allows them to be dismissed or at best patronized by actual decision-makers. Among the strategies discussed is the crucial call to alter the way in which we calculate cost and profit so as to include some sort of monetary valuation of the depletion of natural capital and also some way of assessing impacts on individual and social well-being. One consequence of taking this seriously would be one or another form of carbon taxation.

In the same way, more positively, we need ways of redefining business excellence in terms of sustainability and deliberate encouragement of low-carbon technologies (ch. 14). An economic world in which environmental responsibility was rewarded, was assumed to be a routine aspect of practice that was both ethically defensible *and* profitable, would have a very different flavour from what we have generally seen for most of the last couple of centuries. And it is also an area in which the pressure of the 'ordinary' consumer can make a perceptible difference. More broadly, Porritt rightly underlines the close connection of all this with what we ought to be saying about 'political virtue'. We must find ways of opening up a proper discussion of how to restore a sustainable democratic politics in a world where unbridled economic liberalism has in many contexts eroded the authority of elected governments and led some to believe that there is no alternative to current global capitalism but economies of the most static and protectionist kind.

All these proposals illustrate what an *intelligent* response to the environmental crisis might look like. Porritt is clear that this needs grounding in carefully defined common values and in the renewal of civil society through the articulating and promoting of such values – including the recognition of the interdependence of all things and of the equal significance of diverse kinds of 'capital' – social and human as much as material or natural (see p. 293 for a summary of the argument of Part II of his book). In other words, intelligence comes to life when a kind of empathy and imagination is stirred by a new vision of things: intelligence alone does not generate new vision, and bare argument does not on the whole change things; but vision displayed in new forms of human life and engagement can renew intelligence in the sense I have been giving to the word. And this is where the significance of the perspectives of faith is most obvious.

Creative engagement with nature

Renewing the face of the earth, then, is an enterprise not of imposing some private human vision on a passive nature but of living in such a way as to bring more clearly to light the interconnectedness of all things and their dependence on what we cannot finally master or understand. This certainly involves a *creative* engagement with nature, seeking to work with those natural powers whose working gives us joy, as St Augustine says, in order to enhance human liberty and well-being. But that creative work will always be done in consciousness of costs, seen and unseen, and will not be dominated by fantasies about unconditional domination. It is a vision that, in the Christian context, is founded on the idea of humanity as having a 'priestly' relationship with the natural order: the human agent is created with the capacity to make sense of the environment and to move it into a closer relation with its creator by drawing out of it its capacity to become a sign of love and generosity. This entails so using the things of the earth that they promote justice between human beings – making sense so as to make peace, equity and so on, using the skills of negotiating the environment in order to alleviate suffering and spread resources. Used in this way, the raw material of the environment is seen as serving human need – but only by being used in awareness of its own integrity and its own constraints. It remains itself, but in its use for the sake of healing or justice becomes 'sacramental' of the infinite gift from which it originates. The 'face' of the earth becomes an aspect of the face of God. And a good many

10

theologians have started from here in explaining what the actual sacraments of the Church mean – especially the Eucharist – as the firstfruits of a world of material things that has been given meaning in the context of communicating divine generosity.

All this echoes what St Paul touches on in Romans 8: creation is in some sense frustrated so long as humanity is 'unredeemed'. The world is less than it might be so long as human beings are less than they might be, since the capacity of human beings to shape the material environment into a sign of justice and generosity is blocked by human selfishness. In the doomsday scenarios we are so often invited to contemplate, the ultimate tragedy is that a material world capable of being a manifestation in human hands of divine love is left to itself, as humanity is gradually choked, drowned or starved by its own stupidity. The disappearance of humanity from a globe no longer able to support it would be a terrible negation of God's purpose for a world in which created intelligence draws out the most transformative and rich possibilities in its material home. As is true in various ways throughout the whole created order, humanity and its material context are made so that they may find fulfilment in their relationship. Without each other they are not themselves. And the deliberate human refusal of this shared vocation with and within the material order of things is thus an act of rebellion against the creator.

Which is why Christians are bound to set all this discussion in the context of that divine practice which decisively redeems humankind. God restores relationship with himself through the life, death and resurrection of Jesus: he shows his face to us and – as St Paul says in 2 Corinthians – our own faces are 'unveiled' as we advance towards God. We are revealed for who or what we are. And in this event we become able to reveal what the entire material world is for, to display it as a sign of love by our loving and just use of it – and by our contemplative respect for it and our capacity to let it be. The grace set free in Christ's work allows us to be liberated from the murderous anxiety that drives us to possessive models of engagement. Liberated ourselves, we become able to act liberatingly towards the world we inhabit and whose materiality we share and depend upon. Our own redemption is the re-creation of our intelligence.

The contemporary Greek theologian Christos Yannaras has developed a rich and complex metaphysics of relation, stressing that Christian theology sees the human person as purely abstract if cut off from relation with God and others *and* the material world. He diagnoses the malaise of modern Western society (in politics, philosophy, art and religion) very much in terms of a loss of relation and what goes with it, a loss of the sense of vocation to a sort of 'artistic' transformation of the world. Technology, Yannaras argues, is toxic when it forgets this artistic and transformational dimension – that is (in the terms I've been using here) when it loses its proper human intelligence. But it is a particular image used by Yannaras that perhaps expresses most simply what a Christian account of responsibility in our environment comes down to. In his book of meditations, *Variations on the Song of Songs*, he speaks of how love compels you to see things differently – to love 'the landscapes we have looked at together'. And so if we fall in love with God, even fleetingly, all the sense impressions of this world become part of such a common 'landscape'.[8] We love what we see together with God; and – as I have argued before – if God sees the world he has made as 'very good', I must begin to see it with his eyes and so to sense in it the promise of his beauty. It becomes, in Yannaras's vocabulary, 'a gift of erotic joy' – an encounter with something that generates desire beyond utterance or final fulfilment.

Now it may be a long way from the technicalities of recalculating economic gains in terms of environmental cost to the experience of 'erotic joy' in relation to God. But the distinctive Christian approach to responsibility for our environment has somehow to hold these two languages together. Finally, our care for the world we inhabit is not simply a duty laid upon us but a dimension of life made whole: a redeeming activity grounded in the character of our own redemption, a revelation of the true 'face' of creation as we ourselves undergo the uncovering of our own human face before God. Going back to the root meaning of the Hebrew word, what we're asked to undertake is in fact a conversion – a turning – *towards* the truth: towards the God who is eternally active and giving in ways beyond our concepts, towards the hidden depths of who we ourselves are – and thus towards the face of the earth, seeing it freshly in its unfathomable interrelatedness. As Psalm 104 (vv. 29–30) has it, when God hides his face, creation is locked in fear and slips towards death; when he breathes on creation (when he 'sends his spirit'), creation happens all over again, and the face of the earth is renewed. That turning of the Spirit towards the earth is the movement that carries our love and intelligence in the same direction, so that we can properly make answer for, be responsible for, our world.

2

Visions of the end? Revelation and climate change

TIM GORRINGE

> When the Lamb opened the seventh seal, there was silence in heaven for about half an hour.
>
> (Revelation 8.1, NRSV)

In chapter 4 of Revelation the author tells us that the song of praise before God never ceases (4.8), but now there is silence. 'Heaven seems to hold its breath because of what is about to happen on earth.' Perhaps the author is thinking of the passage in 2 Esdras where the world returns to its 'original silence' as 'at the beginning of creation' when nobody will be left alive (7.30, cf. 6.39).[1] An intensely dramatic image which has caught people's imaginations all the way from the first century to Ingmar Bergman, it could speak about the fear we feel about the possible effects of climate change as represented by James Lovelock in *The Revenge of Gaia*, or Mark Lynas in *Six Degrees*.[2]

But the silence does not last. Seven trumpets are given to seven angels. These may be the seven archangels found in Jewish tradition, a tradition in which trumpets are used to warn or to call. 'All you inhabitants of the world ... When a trumpet is blown, hear!' says Isaiah (18.3). It is the task of prophets as watchmen to call the people to 'give heed to the sound of the trumpet', to hear the warning, says Jeremiah (6.17). 'The word of the LORD came to me,' says Ezekiel:

> Son of man, speak to your people and say to them, If I bring the sword upon a land, and the people of the land take a man from among them, and make him their watchman; and if he sees the sword coming upon the land and blows the trumpet and warns the people; then if any one who hears the sound of the trumpet does not take warning, and the sword comes and takes him away, his blood shall be upon his own head.
>
> (33.2–4)

The prophet is a watchman. So here the angels, and the writer recording what they say, fulfil the role of prophets. They give a warning to the people of God.

Climate change from a theological perspective

How should one address climate change theologically? One could review the theological options: stewardship, the integrity of creation as we find it in Thomas Aquinas, or the intrinsic holiness of creation to which Orthodox theology appeals. We could discuss at great length environmental ethics. We could look at the way in which Trinitarian doctrine bears on it. I choose instead to address the issue through the book of Revelation.

This may well seem a very dubious choice: am I not aligning myself with those fundamentalists who have Rapture stickers on their bumpers? Do I think that the book of Revelation foretold climate change? In the first case, I hope not, and in the second case, of course not. Let me say right at the outset that I take it for granted that the author of Revelation had no inkling of climate change and the original intention of his imagery related to the Roman Empire. In the same way the first Isaiah warned against invasion from the North, and the second Isaiah spoke of the return from exile. Every Scripture text emerges from a particular context. But we read all these texts in the wider context of the divine intention as revealed in Christ: law, wisdom, prophecy, poetry all speak of the engagement of God with humankind and invite us to reflect on that engagement today. Put slightly differently I begin from the presupposition that in Scripture we have words which, as Karl Barth put it in regard to Romans, 'urgently and finally address the very marrow of human civilisation', and not a heap of archaeological rubble only of interest to ancient historians.[3] This applies also, in my view, to the book of Revelation. To be Church is to be defined as the community which lives from this collection of writings. What the doctrine of inspiration very feebly and unimaginatively tries to express is the experience, and therefore the assumption, that the community constantly has things of value to learn from these its founding documents. It learns things despite the fact that the situations in which the text is read constantly change. It was true in the Middle Ages as it is true today that in regard to no ethical issue – whether in sexuality, politics or economics – do we find in Scripture specific prescriptions which the task is simply to follow. What we learn, rather, is the direction we have to look for answers. In Rowland and Roberts' words, Scripture gives us 'something like orientations, models, types, directives, principles, inspirations', the things needed to give us a hermeneutic competence to make decisions about our present.[4] This is true also of what some people consider that very odd book, the Revelation of John.

In thinking about climate change as a Christian I turn to Revelation for three reasons. First of all it is what we call 'apocalyptic' literature. Apocalypse does not mean catastrophe and disaster, as we tend to use the word. It means disclosing, exposing, making manifest, holding up this world to the judgement of God. It has nothing to do with 'the end of the world' or its 'extermination'. As Moltmann puts it: 'What Jewish and Christian apocalyptic intends is not to evoke horror in the face of the end, but to encourage endurance in resistance to the powers of this world.'[5] That is the first key reason for going to Revelation.

The biblical apocalypses emerged from dangerous situations where symbolic imagery was used to interpret present events, and they are voices of desperation and hope. This is why we listen to them and why they have something to say to us. It might be that Revelation is particularly apposite for our times. When the great Dutch scholar Miskotte was asked to give some Bible studies in the ruins of Amsterdam in 1945, he chose Nehemiah – because it is about rebuilding the city. In the same way Revelation may speak to us because, it seems to me, we share with its original hearers a sense that things are beyond our control and there is not much we can do. We share with the original readers or hearers a sense of helplessness in the face of Babylon the Great, which in our day is the whole market system, an idolatrous economy.

Second, apocalyptic literature is basically underground literature, communicating in a symbolic language. Symbols run deeper than words, and the symbols from this particular book have done much to shape the Western imagination. Unfortunately our own rational mindset makes little of them. A fellow member of the Iona Community told me that one of the funniest evensongs he had attended was when the minister read a portion of Revelation and concluded, 'Thank God, we only have three more days of this rubbish!' Such failure to understand the symbols is only too common, so it is worth engaging with them to see if they are quite as opaque as people think.

Third, the book of Revelation is a patchwork of quotations from the Hebrew Bible, and perhaps includes, as we shall see, echoes of what we now know as Synoptic material. The author is scripturally literate. To be Christian, I have already said, is to have our identity given us by the narratives, poems and reflections we call 'Scripture'. We can learn from this author something of what it means to dwell within a tradition. Of course we are never again going to become like the seventeenth-century Puritans, whose discourse was saturated with Scripture, but if we forget it, if it no longer shapes our imaginations, then we forget who we are and we cease to be Church. The book of Revelation, therefore, encourages us in scriptural literacy. There are many good commentaries on Revelation, but I am following the commentary by Bas Wielenga, who I learned from and taught alongside in India and who highlights the connections between the text and our contemporary situation, including climate change.

I have begun with Revelation 8 and what I am going to do is to look at just two short sections of text – first, chapter 8 and a few verses of chapter 9 – and then turn briefly to part of chapters 3 and 4 where the writer talks about the Church. I will try first to see how the text might bear on climate change, and then see what it has to say to us as Christians in the face of it.

The environment and the development agenda

So now, back to our text (Rev. 8.6–12): Four angels, one after the other, blow their trumpets and destruction falls on the earth (v. 7), the sea (v. 8), the rivers (v. 10) and heaven/the sky (v. 12). One-third of all life is affected, but not all life is destroyed. Some scholars assume that the text reflects cosmic occurrences in John's time, such as an eclipse in AD 68 and volcanic eruptions. The prophet is a watchman. He blows the trumpet to warn us of impending danger. 'This text', says Wielenga, 'may encourage us to listen to the warning voices of ecological researchers and to the news about rising sea-levels, pollution of earth and sea and rivers and to respond to them by repenting and calling to repentance, by changing our lifestyles.'[6]

There is no lack of warning: the trumpets have been sounding for quite some time. We know that ice-core records indicate that

CO_2 levels have been the same for thousands of years, but are now 30 per cent above pre-industrial levels. They have risen almost a degree in the past 100 years. The ice sheet covering the Arctic Ocean has lost 40 per cent of its volume over the last 30 years and could be completely gone in decades. In Antarctica three great ice sheets have gone completely. Nobody has modelled what the effect of this ice loss would be. Andrew Simms, Director of the Climate Change programme at the New Economics Foundation, argues that in 100 months from 1 August 2008, atmospheric concentrations of greenhouse gases will begin to exceed a point whereby it is no longer *likely* we will be able to avert potentially irreversible and catastrophic climate change. He and his fellow researchers believe this calculation to be conservative. Jeff Ridley of the Meteorological Office believes that the Copenhagen conference of December 2009 was the last chance we had of avoiding warming rising to 2 °C. That may sound very little, but he is sceptical of our avoiding a rise to 3 °C and believes that were we to reach 4 °C no ecosystem would be able to adapt.

Christian Aid tells us that many of the disasters they are responding to have been caused by extreme weather. The poorest countries suffer because of pollution by the richest. Two-thirds of South Asia's disasters are climate related. As global warming increases the frequency, severity and unpredictability of extreme weather events, and causes sea levels to rise, South Asians will bear the brunt. Bangladesh, for example, is predicted to lose one-tenth of its rice crop and one-third of its wheat output over the next 50 years.

What is the cause of all these problems? Of course, rising populations are part of the equation, but that in turn is bound up with economic development since the eighteenth century. Much of this development is good. For millennia people have gone hungry, for millennia they have suffered and died without understanding either cause or cure. The chance to change that had to be grasped. But two factors distorted the development. First, scientific and technological progress gave people the illusion of total control. People thought the so-called natural world could be reduced to questions of input–output, know-how, cost/benefit, and functionality. Commenting on the imperative for farms to get bigger and the boast that a tiny percentage of the population is now able to feed the rest, Wendell Berry condemns the technology of infinity, which makes us all its slaves. The machine, he comments, has become an anti-God, assuming the shape of the tempter – 'All these things will I give you if you will fall down and worship me.' A limitless technology, he comments, is dependent on a limitless morality, which is to say upon no morality at all. By contrast, the knowledge of our limits is 'the most comely and graceful knowledge that we have, the most healing and the most whole'.[7] In fact, as more and more scientists have been insisting over the past 40 years, many natural processes, and in particular the way in which they interrelate, are very poorly understood. The way feedbacks are hastening climate change comes as a surprise because people thought they had the natural world taped. Rather late they find that they do not at all. At the same time, all forms of technological progress since 1760 or so have been harnessed to a profit-oriented economic rationality, or irrationality, which has had the reproduction and accumulation of capital as its primary goal, and this remains true to this day. What this means is that the ecological crisis is a crisis of a whole world view and a whole world system, which we refer to these days as 'globalization'. The triumphs of Western technology and of market economics have been exported to the whole inhabited earth but may cost the whole inhabited earth.

So totally are we enmeshed in this pseudo-rationality that we have difficulty accepting the facts. We take refuge in denial. Alastair McIntosh reminds us that 88 per cent of British people think climate change is happening but only 41 per cent think human beings cause it. Seven out of ten think the government should take a lead but only 21 per cent support increasing the cost of flying, and only 14 per cent support increasing the cost of petrol. Energy consumption is actually rising. Distances travelled by private car increased by 17 per cent between 1996 and 2004; and the number of passenger kilometres travelled by plane rose from 125 billion to 260 billion worldwide between 1990 and 2000.[8] The political will to change things isn't there because the electorate aren't worried enough. Our economic system, says McIntosh, is infantile. We have what he calls 'consensus trance reality', drifting around in a quasi-hypnotic state while danger accumulates silently ahead of us.[9]

God's redemptive will in the midst of calamities

It is in this situation that the warning is sounded. Revelation is not astrology: it is not foretelling particular events, the catastrophes which might attend climate change. What it does do, however, is prompt us to thought. The message to the churches, 'Wake up!', is addressed to us. The call to repentance is always a call to action. It is a call to reshape our economy, our ways of living, our way of farming. And Revelation puts this call in the framework of an appeal to the exodus. What this does is remind us that these visions of calamities must be read within the framework of God's redemptive will. They are not, as they have often been read, about divine vengeance or destruction.

At this point we have to go back to a verse I skipped earlier, 8.3: 'Another angel came and stood at the altar with a golden censer; and he was given much incense to mingle with the prayers of all the saints.' In chapter 18 incense is one of the commodities sold in Babylon the Great, but here it is given and mingled with the prayers of the saints. Why? As Wielenga says,

> Prayers are often so broken-winged, so mingled with bitterness, so loaded with hatred that they need to be purified, to be focused, to be liberated, to be lifted up in order to become part of that all-inclusive prayer 'thy kingdom come, thy will be done on earth as it is in heaven'. This acceptance of our prayers as they are and their transformation in accordance with God's purpose is a gift from heaven and not something we can buy.[10]

We do not know how to pray as we ought, says St Paul. This is the most fundamental truth in the whole Christian teaching of prayer. All prayer schools begin and end here. Paul says the Spirit prays through us. In Revelation our author says the same thing, but in symbolic language, in terms of the angels giving incense to our prayers. How on earth do we pray in the face of the perils of climate change? We don't know – but God knows, and gives incense to our prayers.

There is an interruption after the fourth trumpet which marks the transition to the last three trumpets. John hears an eagle crying in mid heaven: 'Woe, woe, woe to those who dwell on the earth.' These three woes, which are linked to the three trumpets (see 9.1, 13; 11.14), announce the release of demonic forces which are emerging from the bottomless pit and threaten to overwhelm the earth and its inhabitants.

It is tempting to read this in the light of the Kenneth Horne character from BBC Radio's *Round the Horne* programme who called out,

'We be doomed! We all be doomed!' And the 100 months analysis could be read in this way. But in Scripture the image of the eagle is positive. According to Wielenga:

> Deuteronomy compares God's caring and sustaining concern for his people with an 'eagle that flutters over his young, stretching out its wings, catching them, bearing them' (Deut. 32.11). And Second Isaiah compares the renewal of strength through hope in the LORD with mounting up 'with wings like eagles' (40.31). Woes on the other hand occur as exclamations of fear and as lament over those who are going to die or have died. The woes are an expression of compassionate concern from heaven about what is going to happen to the people on earth and at the same time a call to face it, to bear it till it passes and to repent (see 9.20f.). The woes are addressed to those who are happily and comfortably at home and at ease in Babylon – not only to the climate change deniers, but to all those of us who simply don't sense the urgency in changing our lifestyles. The woes say that heaven is deeply concerned that they wake up to it and mend their ways.[11]

The fifth angel blows his trumpet and John sees 'a star fallen from heaven to earth, and he was given the key of the shaft of the bottomless pit'. Here it is a fallen star, in 20.1 an angel coming down from heaven who holds the key of the bottomless pit. The abyss or bottomless pit is a metaphor for the place from whence human wickedness draws its inspiration. It is, as it were, a deep reservoir of evil which reinforces everything which opposes and obstructs the purpose of God. As Walter Wink teaches us, it is a way of speaking of the consolidated negative spirituality which has us in its grip.

The smoke which rises up from the bottomless pit is a counter-image to the 'smoke of the incense' which rose with the prayers of the saints before God's throne (8.4). What rises from the abyss is the opposite. It stands for the spirituality of evil which at times spreads on earth and threatens to overwhelm the spirituality of the prayer 'thy kingdom come, thy will be done'. Remember D. H. Lawrence in Germany in 1923:

> It is as if life had retreated eastwards. As if the Germanic life were slowly ebbing away from contact with western Europe, ebbing to the deserts of the east . . . Returning again to the fascination of the destructive east, that produced Attila . . . at night you feel strange things stirring in the darkness, strange feelings stirring out of this still unconquered

Black Forest. You stiffen your backbone and you listen to the night. There is a sense of danger. It is not the people. They don't seem dangerous. Out of the very air comes a sense of danger, a queer, *bristling* feeling of uncanny danger.

Something has happened. Something has happened which has not yet eventuated. The old spell of the old world has broken, and the old, bristling, savage spirit has set in . . . Something has happened to the human soul, beyond all help . . . It is a fate; nobody now can alter it . . . At the same time, we have brought it about ourselves – by a Ruhr occupation, by an English nullity, and by a German false will. We have done it ourselves. But apparently it was not to be helped.

This, says Wink, is an example of the Domination system. 'This spirit-killing atmosphere penetrates everything, teaching us not only what to believe, but what we can value and even what we can see.'[12]

In Scripture this is spoken of in terms of hardening our hearts. As Wielenga points out, there are many examples in history of such hardening of the heart gripping a society and leading to destructive madness.[13] Perhaps our addiction to consumerism, our implicit or explicit denial of climate change, should be understood as one of them. The ecological crisis is already, as Jürgen Moltmann said many years ago, not simply a technological crisis but a religious crisis of the paradigm in which people in the Western world, and increasingly Asia as well, put their trust and live. It is a moral and spiritual crisis. For this reason it cannot be met either by bland optimism or by faith in technology. It has to be met with a stronger and deeper faith appealing to quite different grounds of hope. Here the author of Revelation speaks to us. He teaches us to 'lift up our heads', and to be open for God's new beginning in the breakdown of the world system constructed in the past 200 years.

The angels release plagues which cause a disintegration of creation, a return to chaos, but the locusts are 'told not to harm the grass of the earth or any green growth or any tree, but only those people who do not have the seal of God on their foreheads' (Rev. 9.4, NRSV). The target of the locusts is humans and not non-human creation. The imagery is difficult but the main point seems to be that there is still scope for repentance. The question to us is whether we understand the ecological crisis as God's warning judgement, as a call to repent, to turn away from the sins of which that crisis is the consequence.

Destruction of destructive powers

I am now going to turn back from chapters 8 and 9 to chapter 3, because I want to ask where the Church stands in all of this. I turn especially to the warning to the church in Laodicea:

> 'And to the angel of the church in Laodicea write: The words of the Amen, the faithful and true witness, the beginning of God's creation. I know your works: you are neither cold nor hot. Would that you were cold or hot! So, because you are lukewarm, and neither cold nor hot, I will spew you out of my mouth. For you say, I am rich, I have prospered, and I need nothing; not knowing that you are wretched, pitiable, poor, blind, and naked.'
>
> (Rev. 3.14–17)

Laodicea was a prosperous city, known for its banks, textiles and medicine. The church here gets the most severe judgement of all the seven churches addressed by the author.

It will be spewed out because it is 'lukewarm and neither cold nor hot'. What this seems to mean is that the city's prosperity causes its people neither to have the passion to change the world nor to know the bleak misery of despair. They are at ease in Zion. Throughout the letters to the seven churches Christ is spoken of as the Lord of creation, recalling the letters to the Colossians and Ephesians. The problem with the Laodiceans is that they lack concern for God's creation. As Wielenga says:

> They accumulate wealth in their banks, they are skilled in appropriating the resources of creation, but they do not know how needy they are. They lack the solidarity in hope with the creation which is groaning to be set free (Rom. 8.18–25). Their lukewarm indifference to their fellow creatures may actually be the sort of spirituality which leads to the destruction of the earth (cf. 11.18). Therefore, says the author, in fact you are *wretched, pitiable, poor, blind and naked*. We have to ask whether this does not apply to us, who in our self-centred consumerism are indifferent to what happens to the creation whose resources we exploit. Our eyes need to be opened, we need wisdom, we need to repent and to open the door and to learn what it is to share in the messianic meal.[14]

To do so at the present time might be to seriously accept the path of contraction and convergence, to find ways to share the blessings of creation and not, like Samson, to take everything down with us.

John goes on to a vision of God in heaven. As Wielenga argues, many people find the royal imagery employed here out of date and alienating, but what the author wants to convey is the message that there is not only the power of Rome or Washington, not only the power of the giant transnational companies, but a different reality beyond the grasp of those destructive powers. There is a throne in heaven, there is an alternative power at work in history.[15] It is the power of love – as the vision of the Lamb will reveal – a power which aims at redeeming life and sustaining it. Around the throne is the rainbow, the sign of God's covenant with the earth and all life (Gen. 9.13). This vision assures us that God's majesty is equalled by his mercy (Ecclus. 2.18), or rather that majesty is revealed in God's benevolent reign of care for the earth. The door to heaven is open. As long as heaven is thought to be closed we can be under the illusion that the destructive powers are the only ones that count, but John opens our eyes both to the forces of destruction and to the throne in heaven with the rainbow which will prevail.

In the vision the 24 elders cry out, 'You are worthy, our Lord and God, to receive glory and honour and power, for you created all things, and by your will they existed and were created' (4.11). Wielenga explains:

> The author reminds us that we are called to give glory and honour and power to God in our relationship to all that God has called into existence. Hundreds of thousands of species are threatened with extinction today. *By your will they existed and were created* sing the elders. Why does the church not join more eagerly in the worldwide protests against the extinction of species meant to praise without ceasing the holiness of God? How do we learn to cast the crowns of money, power and of science and technology before the throne of God?

As we know, Revelation is a favourite text for preachers predicting the end of the world, but this is a gross misuse of the book. When it speaks of destruction it is thinking of the destruction of destructive powers.

> The powers of militarism, of Babylon and Rome, the beast from the abyss, the power of poisonous propaganda, the idolatry of wealth and might – such are the rebellious forces which stand in the way of God's kingdom. They stand condemned by the witness, death and resurrection of the Messiah and his witnesses. For them there is no

future – thank God. Their destruction by God's judgement opens the future for the earth and humankind. The secret of that liberative judgement is the covenant, his promise to redeem and not to destroy. That is what becomes visible at the sound of the last trumpet: '*the ark of his covenant*' as the '*temple in heaven was opened*'.[16]

Hope, repentance and action

Revelation is a call to hope grounded on faith, not optimism. It is a call to repentance and action. Action means in the first instance all the obvious things – recycling, insulating, using cars and aeroplanes less, being responsible about our carbon footprint. Much more it means acting to bring about change – trying to bring about that huge shift in public consciousness which is necessary before that change can happen. The Transition Town movement is one such movement in which we can involve ourselves. It operates from the grass roots, from the bottom up, and it has the potential to transform communities and our energy patterns. It could represent the kind of moral tipping point, in the right not the wrong direction, which we need. Christians have not invented or led this movement but they should engage in it, bringing to it hope in the God who raised Jesus Christ from the dead as the ground of action in the face of imminent danger. With reference to this hope I want to end with some wonderful words from Moltmann's *God in Creation*. And I will remind you first of the wonderful story about Luther and the apple tree. Luther was asked what he would do if he knew the world was going to end the next day. His answer was, 'Plant an apple tree.' This expresses his faith in God's purposes for the creation. As Moltmann says:

> In the present situation of our world facile consolation is as fatal as melancholy hopelessness. No one can assure us that the worst will not happen. According to all the laws of experience: it will. We can only trust that even the end of the world hides a new beginning if we trust the God who calls into being the things that are not, and out of death creates new life . . . In view of the deadly dangers threatening the world, Christian remembrance makes ever present the death of Christ in its apocalyptic dimensions, in order to draw forth from his resurrection from the dead hope for 'the life of the world to come', and from his rebirth to eternal life hope for the rebirth of the cosmos . . . Life out of this hope then means already acting here and today in accordance with that world of justice and righteousness and peace, contrary to

appearances, and contrary to all historical chances of success. It obliges us to solemnly abjure the spirit, logic and practice of the nuclear system of deterrence and all other systems of mass annihilation. It means an unconditional Yes to Life in the face of the inescapable death of all the living. That is the deeper meaning of the legendary Luther saying about 'the apple tree' which he would plant today even if he knew that the world was going to end tomorrow.[17]

3

Consider the lilies of the field: Reading Luke's Gospel and saving the planet

MARY C. GREY

'Consider the lilies . . .' (Luke 12.22–31); the flowers in the grounds of Tantur Ecumenical Institute, outside Jerusalem, near the Bethlehem checkpoint, are thought to be the biblical lilies. Whether they are the same flowers or not, what matters is that they are flowers of beauty, springing up every year in the early awakening of spring with a vibrant splash of colour. Jesus in the Gospels of both Luke and Matthew singles them out, and other scriptural writers are lyrical in wondering at lilies, roses of Sharon, olives, fruit trees and cedars of Lebanon. All are appreciated and valued as part of a diversity of myriad forms of life of divine creation; living forms of the life-giving sustenance and presence of God. But why 'consider the lilies' in this time of crisis of climate change? Indeed, why consult Scripture at all? Surely science and effective legislation are what is needed?

And in any case, what possible clue could be gained from reflecting on a civilization and period whose ecological footprint was far lighter than ours, a time when there may have been injustice and exploitation in terms of land usage, when species may have been hunted to extinction, but when there was no threat from a rise in earth's temperature sufficient to threaten the planet's very survival. So, I first answer the question, *Why Scripture?* And then the question, *Why Luke?* I will bring into my explorations some of my experiences both in Palestine and in the desert of north-west India, in Rajasthan, as part of my work with the charity Wells for India.[1]

Why Scripture?

We read scriptural texts now with far greater awareness of their context and of the gap between that context and our own. We know that the authors of the texts as we have them – there may have been several writers, and an editorial process over time – brought the needs and questions of their communities to their stories and memories, and wrote the texts as answers to those needs. These communities may themselves have been experiencing danger, tribulations or persecutions. Some texts tried to keep their hopes alive – for example the prophets Isaiah and Ezekiel at the time of the Babylonian exile. We are now reading sacred texts at a time of an unprecedented ecological crisis that threatens the planet's very survival. Every recent analysis indicates that the climate situation is worsening. The Massachusetts Institute of Technology's Joint Program on the Science and Policy of Global Change has recently revised its projection, indicating that if we stick with business as usual, in terms of carbon emissions, average surface temperatures on earth by 2100 will hit levels far beyond anything humans have ever experienced.[2]

The uptake of carbon by the oceans is weaker, feedbacks from the land system as temperature rises are stronger, cumulative emissions of greenhouse gases over the century are higher, and the cooling that results from aerosol emissions and that offsets the warming is lower. These factors, taken separately, might not be so threatening; but, as we know, all things are connected, and they are interacting in a cumulative way to lead to the chance of higher temperatures. But if we put this in the context of the current anxiety over the economic recession, bank collapse and unemployment, it is clear that climate change has been pushed into the background, and is now at a far lower level in the hierarchy of our concerns (a recent US poll put climate change just twentieth in such a list of concerns).

It is not as if we are in any doubt about what we should be doing. Hal Harvey of Climateworks (based in California) declares that we need energy-efficient housing, car fuel efficiency, effective renewable energy policy, a price on carbon – polluting should not be free – and a policy he calls decoupling: he means that power utilities should help homeowners save energy rather than encouraging them to consume it. We may have our own variation on this list and our own priorities, but the problem is actually the will to act, the will to put these policies into practice. It is ourselves we are fighting, as George Monbiot has written, taking a very pessimistic view as to the possibility of a change of heart.[3] But we should never allow public policy to be separated from personal transformation. And that is where Scripture comes in. Sacred texts will not give us direct answers, but they offer clues, and resources for change. These are texts we read all the time in our churches and homes, year after year, yet, sadly, with scant awareness of their potential to change our hearts, minds and public policies to reflect an ethic of living justly with the earth. Above all, sacred texts recall us to the sacred trust God has given us with regard to the earth and all its diversity of life-forms.

Why Luke?

So to my second question, Why Luke? (I admit that several other choices are possible.) I wanted to use a text that Christians love and could regard as a journey companion on this quest for changed lifestyles and policies. First, the journey theme is central to Luke. From the beginning, where Joseph and Mary set off for Bethlehem, to the end, where the disciples rush back from Emmaus to Jerusalem, there is a many-levelled quest going on. (And Luke is intentionally rewriting the Exodus story.) Second, Luke, though some question whether he was ever in Palestine, is writing *about* a poor peasant community, mostly landless, yet *for* rich landowners (his patron, Theophilus, may have been one such), as well as for city dwellers, so his view of social harmony is closely linked with a just land ethic. Because of this social mix he appeals to us all, making it difficult to lay the blame *out there*, or on a single sector of society.

Third, Luke offers resources for a liberation theology in the context of climate change. Liberation theology has from its inception put the poorest categories of people at its heart, seeing God's passion for justice at the centre of faith, not at its periphery. But in our present crisis, nature, the earth and her exploited resources have become the new category of poverty.[4] Nature is the new poor. Earth creatures in their ruined habitats are now the focus of attention for liberation theology. This means that core theological categories acquire a different focus. The cross of Christ is drawn to where nature is suffering, from rising temperatures, to the nearly destroyed Amazonian forest, to the growing deserts of the world, to polluted air and seas. For too long has nature *not* been factored into the need for redemption.

And, finally, Luke's Gospel is a Gospel of peace. From the angels' song at Christmas, 'peace on earth to all people of goodwill', to the greeting of the Easter Jesus, 'Peace be with you', this is Luke's intent:

so now I suggest a re-reading of Luke with reconciliation with the earth as our hope, and action in the face of devastating climate change as our goal.

Let us now follow Luke's invitation to revisit Nazareth, and be present at what has become known as the Nazareth Manifesto (Luke 4.18–30). Into the synagogue of his home town of Nazareth enters the young Rabbi Jesus, and the level of expectancy of the local people, presumably including the neighbours, and family members themselves, is high. He is given the scroll and it falls open at the reading for the day, Isaiah 61.1–7: 'The Spirit of the Lord is upon me, because he has anointed me to preach good news to the poor . . .'

We know the text so well. Luke could never have envisaged the impact this text would continue to have as the agenda for liberation theology. It was inspirational for the campaign of Jubilee 2000, Cancel the Debt (since its reference to 'Proclaim the acceptable year of the Lord' invoked the Jubilee laws of justice for the land), and there is a consistent thread of interpretation, invoking this passage as part of the struggle of all social justice movements across the continents. The late Michael Prior (a Vincentian priest and activist for Palestine), for example, read it as a text inspiring a new revolutionary order:

> The New Order inaugurated by Jesus of Nazareth, will not be brought in by the rhetoric of the most eloquent of liberation theologians alone. In contemporary society, the evangelization of the poor will come about only through the combined efforts of competent people who share the vision of Jesus.[5]

A similar interpretation is opted for by James Massey, an Indian Dalit theologian (Dalits are the former Untouchables of India) who, in his Dalit Bible commentary, sees the Nazareth Manifesto as Jesus reaching out to the most oppressed, outcastes and outsiders, in his case referring specifically to the Dalit communities.[6] Can we read it now in our own crisis to inspire action for change and climate justice?

Jesus as a landless prophet and the situation of Palestine today

What were the issues for Jesus and the community for which Luke wrote regarding justice for the earth? Even though this was a community treading lightly on the earth compared with ourselves, ecological justice was far from an abiding principle. Ecological concerns for well-being have always included humans and non-humans alike in their environment. And this connection has always been vulnerable to exploitation. Luke portrays Jesus as inheriting the prophetic dreams, for example, of Isaiah, as the Nazareth Manifesto has shown us. Isaiah 11 speaks of the great messianic vision of harmony with creation, to include all animals in the peaceable kingdom. The Jubilee laws – already referred to – of Leviticus 25 extend justice to the liberation of the land, as well as the setting free of slaves and the cancellation of debts: 'The Sabbath of the land shall provide food for you, for yourself and for your male and female slaves and for your hired servant and the sojourner who lives with you; for your cattle also and for the beasts that are in your land all its yield shall be for food' (Lev. 25.6–7).

This vision of the flourishing of land, animals and people together, is the context of a culture of peace that I am suggesting Luke is also working towards: the ideal that swords be turned into ploughshares, that each shall sit under his or her own fig tree.[7] In Edward Echlin's book *Earth Spirituality: Jesus at the Centre* we are given a vivid, imaginative picture of the ecology of Palestine in the time of Jesus: he evokes the creatures of the desert, the diversity of birds, dogs and foxes, goats, water creatures and snakes.[8] All of these, the soil and animal communities, enter the connectedness of justice for the earth.

But the question is, how did Luke's Jesus relate to this richness of creatures, tree and landscape? How did they shape his faith in God, and the lifestyle of his followers? And how was this dependent on ecological justice? Jesus was mostly addressing poor farmers, hirelings of the Romans, landless people, dependent on having a day's work in the vineyard, in the wheat fields, in the olive groves, labouring all night to catch a few fish in the sea of Galilee, or being swineherds for the pork destined for the tables of the Roman occupier. Here I am tracing links between poverty and people's connections with the earth. The parable of the lost coin (Luke 15.8–10) offers a window on to the poverty of women. The value of the lost coin was equal to one denarius. The German liberation theologian Luise Schottroff explains that this was the daily wage that a worker in the vineyard would expect – and he would not be in regular work. Two hundred denarii was the average *yearly* income of a worker on the land. This would not have been sufficient to sustain his family even in bread. So there must have been small plots of land, where women and children also worked. (Children were expected to work from the age of six.) Women worked also in textile production as weavers, but in both cases they earned less than men. So the point of Luke's story (chapter 5) is that the woman had lost the equivalent of a labourer's daily wage, a sum which she had worked harder and longer to get. Poverty is measured in terms of hunger, housing, poor clothing – and the misery of debt that forced people into slavery. The social stigma attached to many trades is also relevant.

There are parallels between first-century Palestine and contemporary rural Rajasthan (north-west India). In the impoverished communities I know well, people are poor through a mixture of the harsh conditions of the desert (they experience both drought and floods, now exacerbated through climate change), caste-based poverty, the consequences of colonization and unjust local rulers, as well as the dangers of racial violence or bandits (the robbers on the road to Jericho come to mind). Failure of the harvest brings famine and over-reliance on the moneylender: because debt spirals out of control, people are forced to sell themselves as bonded labourers for a lifetime, even passing on the debt to their children. For women, the option is prostitution or being trafficked. It is no accident that Luke's Jesus has many stories about debt. In the first century dung-collectors and tanners were also despised, because of the foul smell connected with their activities. If a woman was married to any one of these, she had the right to claim divorce.[9] This recalls the current despising of Dalits in India, especially because they skin dead cows and clean latrines. The parallel is important, because it shows that the inability of poor people to move out of poverty is linked not only with failure to earn a regular wage, but also with entrenched notions of purity and pollution.

For poor people, simply getting enough to eat was the main problem. Meat was rare: as we see in the parable of the fattened calf (Luke 15), the elder brother complained that no calf had been killed for him. Poor people could not afford wheat or meat, and ate barley bread. They were often reduced to eating locusts for meat, and older domestic animals. In rural Rajasthan, diet is still a huge problem. Most women are undernourished and in consequence are anaemic: many die in childbirth and the child mortality rate is very high because of poor diet, and because clean water and access to medical care are lacking.

The absence of medical care for poor people in the time of Jesus is part of the reason that the sick flocked to him in hope of healing. But the biggest contrast between rich and poor in any society is in terms of security. The rich can afford to prepare for the lean years by storing grain in barns (Luke 12.16–21). Their houses are proof against storms and floods. They wear clothing both beautiful and warm – as we see from the parable of Dives and Lazarus (Luke 16.19–31). Contrast the poor men I see on the streets of Delhi every year. (Admittedly this is a city, not a village – it is easier to find hospitality and shelter in a village.) It is winter and they are huddled on the pavements around a small fire built from a few sticks. They pull their cloaks around them to shut out the wind and try to boil a small pan of water to make some warm tea (*chai*). Or take the villages. Here the people's small huts are normally adequate to provide shelter – but not in a storm, or when rivers burst their banks: then they are swept away as easily as a child's house of paper. Of course these parallels are not exact, and Luke was writing, from Greece, about conditions in the time of Jesus' Palestine, about which, perhaps, he knew very little personally: but the parables certainly evoke the harsh realities of poverty.

The point to be stressed is that the basis of life was the organic connection between nature and the well-being of people and all life-forms. This is *still* the basis of life, but we in our comfort zones have concealed it through false expectations that supermarkets will deliver what we want to eat throughout the entire year, houses will continue to be warmed by fossil fuels, and environmental problems can be confined to the poor southern countries. *No more.* Of course, the problem of global warming did not exist in first-century Palestine, but the inability to tackle it effectively *now* is paralleled by the divisions of rich and poor in New Testament times; and the unwillingness of the rich – be they Roman or Jewish – to change their lifestyles to allow poor people to have the barest level of dignified humanity constituted the same kind of barrier as it does today.

But if we look at Palestine/Israel today, a worse picture of environmental woe, exacerbated by politics, exists. In the narrative of poverty of the first century, the focus was on food, clothing, housing and the curing of serious illness and disability; the focus today is more strikingly on issues of water and land but also on food and housing. The lack and poor quality of water is now recognized globally as the most important cause of poor health, illness and child mortality. Three million children die from dysentery every year – 6,000 a day from water-borne diseases like gastroenteritis. Eighty per cent of diseases in the poor south are water related.[10]

We know how important land was for Jesus: Luke portrays him as always on the move, from the Jordan to the desert, to Nazareth, through Galilee's villages and eventually to Jerusalem. The Palestinian environmentalist Hwaa Irfan writes of the same strong organic relationship today 'between a land and its people generation after generation. The respect for and the understanding of their ecosystem shape their lives. When respected, the environment is the source of well-being, but when abused it becomes the source of ill health and discord.'[11]

Palestine, he continues, once covered 26,320 kilometres of land and had 704 kilometres of inland water. Formerly there were rolling woodlands covered with thickets, forests, and grasslands. When the 1948 war displaced between 700,000 and 800,000 Palestinians, this meant a massive influx of refugees into a fragile ecosystem and the beginning of the destruction of over 400 Palestinian villages. By the time of the 1967 Israeli occupation, Gaza was on the brink of a water crisis with frequent outbreaks of water-borne diseases and increased soil alkalinity and salinity. Because of the Israeli occupation, and the ensuing expansion and construction projects, Palestine now suffers from a weakened agricultural system, problems with waste-water disposal and from solid waste pollution, and water security issues.

According to research carried out by the Palestinian Hydrology Group, there are many cases in which water purchases amount to 10 per cent of a family's expenses. And this is where families can afford to buy water; for many it is too expensive. It is in Gaza where the issue is most critical, as we saw with the war that took place in the winter of 2008–9. Thus many families are forced to reduce their consumption, making it harder for them to meet their basic needs of personal hygiene, house cleaning, and the washing of dishes and clothes. Land is crucial to the Palestinian economy. During the Intifada, Israeli forces uprooted acres of olive trees, grapevines, palm trees, almonds, oranges, figs, strawberries, guava and bananas. The grief that this caused can scarcely be described. In cases of cleared land documented by the Palestinian Ministry of Agriculture 271,797 trees have been uprooted. Palestinians now have no sovereignty and limited access to the region's natural resources.

This is just a brief snapshot of what is happening to land in the West Bank that Jesus knew well. Space does not allow a wider focus to include the whole of Israel: what I hope to have shown, however, is that the suffering caused by climate change can be exacerbated where reconciliation and justice with the earth are blocked by the political situation.

Reading Luke and saving the planet

After this brief snapshot of Palestine then and now, I return to the central issue: how does reading Luke affect the agenda of global warming? We have looked at the context for Jesus' ministry, but what of its content? If, as Sallie McFague suggests, we see the world, the earth, metaphorically as the Body of God, then Jesus is this body in which we dwell, this dream enfleshed. Jesus is the pattern, the embodiment of the Body of God: the incarnate body has a Christic pattern. Looking closely at this Christic pattern, the pattern of Jesus' ministry, we see a focus on bodies – they matter, their health, well-being and flourishing matter. Jesus wants the bodies of all creatures to be fed, nourished and healed. What is more, the Christic body focuses on the poorest, most underfed, vulnerable and rejected bodies. The Christic body through the ages has sought out new situations where the Body is rejected and suffering. Hence now the threatened earth herself, the cosmic Body, threatened, exploited, with growing areas of desertification (the result of war, occupation and land clearances), is the concern of ministry.

The first point about Luke, then, is the focus on peace between heaven and earth. Not only did the angels sing of peace on the earth, suggesting that a peace that could once only be thought of as existing in heaven, can now be sought through reconciliation with the earth,[12] but there is a hint of this in Jesus' triumphal ride into Jerusalem (Luke 19.38), immediately followed by his weeping over Jerusalem – 'Would that even today you knew the things that make for peace!' There is even a possibility that the line in the Lord's Prayer – 'on earth as it is in heaven' – could be suggesting a less dualistic hierarchy between heaven and earth. I add that Luke's is a Gospel of non-violence:

Luke's Jesus will not conquer with the sword. Remember that when Peter cuts off the slave's ear, Jesus heals it immediately, saying, 'No more of this!' (Luke 22.50–52).

Second, Luke's is a message of urgency. Action has to take place now. Zacchaeus (Luke 19) is told, 'Today salvation has come to this house', but only when he has given back fourfold what he has taken unjustly. Yet there is no easy way for us to pay back or restore instantaneously the damage we have inflicted on air and sea through the overconsumption of greenhouse gases: we can only begin the payback process, but *today*!

Third, in case we are on the verge of despair, Luke's Gospel is one of perseverance and prayer. The story of the unjust judge and the widow (18.1–8) comes to mind. So too, however, do Jesus' injunctions to keep praying. Palestinians today are developing a spirituality, that of *sumud*, or steadfastness. Even if there seems no solution, not even any hope, keep doing what you know is right. Your course of action is one for the long haul. Take a deep breath and a long breath. I will return to this.

Fourth, Luke's Gospel spells out the spirituality of the sacrificial lifestyle needed in a time of climate change. Radical simplicity is the key: 'Take nothing for your journey, no staff, nor bag, nor bread, nor money; and do not have two tunics' (Luke 9.3).

Mostly tradition weakens these commands. They are not for us, goes the dismissive thinking, only for the radical ascetics who, through the ages, have come back to this text and followed its inspiration – St Francis, for example. But now, we do not have a choice. For the past three decades, lifestyle movements (like Canon Horace Dammers' Life Style Movement, with its slogan 'Live simply that others may simply live') have been urging this message upon us. Slowly we begin to heed it. We do care about food miles. (And air miles.) We *are* in process of educating ourselves not to need strawberries in January, and are committed to fair trade. But there is a very long way to go. In our country we can still make choices – but boatloads of refugees sinking in the seas between Somalia and Sicily tell us that for many countries there are no choices for poor people and life is unsustainable. This text of Luke's stands as a challenge: what more will we let go of, to make life on earth sustainable for the most vulnerable people?

Next, almost a counterbalance to the previous urging. Luke's Gospel is one of hospitality and welcome. Jesus' birth is announced to poor shepherds – shepherds were a despised trade in New Testament times. Mary and Joseph are welcomed in a poor home – it may not have been a stable. Jesus and his followers depend on hospitality wherever they go. The text cited above continues: 'Whatever house you enter, first say, "Peace be to this house!" And if a son of peace is there, your peace shall rest upon him; but if not, it shall return to you' (Luke 10.5). But this is not just an ethic for missionary journeys, or a reference to Middle Eastern hospitality, vital though this is. Haunting Luke's Jesus is the vision of Isaiah, and Isaiah 11 with its messianic vision of peace is not far away. Peace is reconciliation with the earth. Peace means reverencing the earth's hospitality that we have abused. Peace means paying back our debts to the earth before it is too late. Scripture is redolent with texts and poetry extolling the hospitality of the earth, which is of course the hospitality of God: the 'God saw that it was good' of the creation stories. Can we ever imagine the grief of God at what we have done with divine hospitality?

The next point is a vital one. Jesus is incarnate as the wisdom of God and is still present in Spirit today. Luke presents him full of organic wisdom. For Jesus, rooted in the soil, animal and agricultural community of the Galilean hills, the project of the coming kingdom was described in natural images: 'The kingdom of God is like . . .' We miss the point if we think that he chose the mustard seed, the ravens, the lilies or the vineyards only because he lived in a rural idyll, far from our present setting. Yes, the images he evoked were part of the life-world of his hearers and followers. But they also form an organic part of the body of the whole. The health of the body is directly related to the health of the parts. The Wisdom literature is clear that the fish of the sea, like the birds of the air, are our teachers (see Job 12). Wisdom, says Jeffrey Schloss, Professor of Biology at Westmont College, 'is living in a way that corresponds to how things are'.[13] The organic world view of the Bible does not have to be seen as naive, pre-industrial romanticism. I have tried to show that some of the same tensions between rich and poor, a rapacious greed that has no compassion for victims, are no different today. The parables and healings of Jesus are more than charming stories: like the Magnificat, they destabilize the mighty, remove false authority from the powerful and offer liberation from oppressive hierarchies. A mustard seed, and a woman with yeast become symbols of the kingdom of heaven (Luke 13). Women, Samaritans, lepers are ministered to in a universalist vision of a world where all can share the messianic feast. And animals may be present not only as food to be consumed! Recalled to the wisdom-inspired, organic, interconnected world view we cannot go back to the market-dominated one, if we are committed to transforming the current predicament. *It can never be business as usual.* This is why we need a faith-based view, a biblically based economics of care – strong enough, for example, to oppose the airlines who tell us that although the number of flights has dropped slightly and corporate jets are not used so frequently, when the economy picks up (maybe next year?) things will return to normal.

Luke has two final lessons for us. The journeying Jesus sets his face for Jerusalem and a violent death. The Gospels cite many passages of coming tribulations that have a very contemporary feel: 'Nation will rise against nation, and kingdom against kingdom; there will be great earthquakes, and in various places famines and pestilences; and there will be terrors and great signs' (21.10–11).

But lest we fall into apocalyptic mode (this is Luke, not the book of Revelation!), assuming a fatalistic sense of doom, let us note that Jesus puts this not only into the context of the persecution his followers would undergo, but of how they would be comforted and strengthened in their resistance: the spirituality of *sumud*, endurance and steadfastness again. I see this as an invitation to us to stand firm in our chosen path of resistance to ecocidal policies. Jesus did go forward to the Garden of Gethsemane and he was comforted by an angel. The angels of peace are never far away in Luke and his Gospel is redolent with encouragement that God's Providence is with those who carry the cross with Jesus. I have suggested that the cross of Christ is planted, in these days of global warming, in the places of greatest suffering, standing in the path of a tsunami or a hurricane, or in a flimsy boat on the ocean. The eco-theologian Larry Rasmussen writes evocatively of what the power of the cross can mean today:

> Until we enter the places of suffering and experience them with those who are entangled there, as God does, our actions will not be co-redemptive . . . The only power that can truly heal and keep the creation is power that intimately knows its degradation . . . the only effective power is power instinctively drawn to these hellish sites,

there to call forth to the desperate and needy themselves extraordinary yet common powers that they did not even know they had. Perhaps this is why, in the emotive region of the cross and in the awful silence before the dying Christ, one hears the seismic whisper of none other than the power of God . . .[14]

This is not to glorify suffering but to assert that the deliberately chosen path of suffering cannot be ignored – for the sake of the preservation of the delicately interwoven ecosystems and the survival of the planet. It is not to impale any group of vulnerable people on the cross of the world. But it is to say that the path of protest and resistance in the name of the passionate love of all creation's survival will make suffering inevitable, if we are to break the cycle of violence and the values of global capitalism and market consumerism that keep the current unjust system in place.[15]

And finally the Spirit. Luke has a special drama for the Spirit. Jesus is conceived, baptized in the Spirit and then, full of the power of the Spirit, returns to Nazareth, where we began the story. And then silence. Until, after the resurrection, the Spirit is poured out to all the faithful followers (Acts 2). And in today's crisis the Spirit is our guide and inspirer. First of all, as Spirit of truth, that we speak with truth and not denial about global warming. (We have suffered enough setbacks from this.) The Spirit encourages imagination, that we think and imagine another way of being. (The spirituality of *sumud* also evokes this.) I think of the creativity of many groups: my friends in Christian Ecology Link, of Operation Noah launching the Ark on the River Thames – so many efforts to demonstrate that there is another way to coexist within the earth's limits.

The Spirit need not today be imaged as gentle dove (the scriptural image), but as 'the Wild Bird who heals'.[16] She can be goose, swan, even eagle or bird of prey, arising in many spiritualities today in an interreligious perspective. This is the Spirit calling us to protect the wetland and wilderness, the diversity of creatures that live there, the pure air and unpolluted water that they need. This is a new revelation of the Spirit as the green face of God: 'the Wild Bird who heals' emerging, calling for the end of short-sighted theologies of the stewardship of creation, and for the ignition of full-blown ethics and economics that replace the destructive policies of the present. The Spirit as kindling the renewal of the face of the earth – more literally than the psalmist meant it! As Mark Wallace says: 'If we allow the Spirit's biophilic insurgency to redefine us as pilgrims and sojourners rather than wardens and stewards, our legacy to posterity might well be healing and life-giving, and not destructive of the hopes of future generations.' [17]

With the Wild Bird of the Spirit set free for prophetic action today, we have left the pages of Luke. But the gentle Doctor has one more message in conclusion. Luke's Gospel is often called the Gospel of the heart, so redolent is it of compassion and love. Luke's Jesus wants to cast fire on the earth (12.49), but it is a fire for justice for the vulnerable. His compassion for widows, lepers, despised ethnic groups, can fuel both the fire of our compassion for the victims of global warming, and an anger that demands change and transformation. Let us recall the emotions of the two disciples who met the risen Jesus at Emmaus, and knew him in the breaking of the bread: 'Did not our hearts burn within us?' Is it not those same burning hearts we need to commit ourselves to working for a stable earth temperature with an increase of no more than two degrees, and the same energy that sent them racing back to Jerusalem to proclaim a message of hope?

Conclusion: Consider the lilies . . .

And so, we come full circle. Consider the lilies: as I said, the anemone (*A. coronaria*) is traditionally identified as the 'lily of the field'. Widespread in the Mediterranean region, its flowers can be found in several colours. Recent research in Israel has shown that there is a genetic basis for this variation which accounts for the dominance of a certain colour in a particular region. Around Jerusalem, for instance, the scarlet form is more frequent than the blue, while on the slopes near Capernaum the hillside is flecked with the blue and white flowers. Here I'm using them as a symbol of natural beauty, of the providential care of God for the entirety of creation as well as a symbol of the wisdom of nature. Matthew writes of the lilies of the field in the context of the Sermon on the Mount (Matt. 6.25–33). Luke's context is no less radical: Luke's community will face persecution. Some of his hearers are wealthy – the temptation for them of the accumulation of riches is pervasive. For all, the priority is commitment to the kingdom – this is how Luke's telling of the parable ends (12.31). But within that, the wisdom of creation – forgotten and despised through the centuries – is to inspire and guide us through this crisis into God's redeemed future for *all* created life.

4

Hope, hype and honesty reporting global change: A still point on a turning planet

MARTIN REDFERN

My background is in geology, though I have been a science journalist for three decades. As far as religion is concerned, my position might be best summarized by the answer the late Arthur C. Clarke gave when he was asked whether he believed in God. No, he replied, but I am very interested in him. And it's a similar interest that keeps me coming to conferences on science and religion, and led me to apply for and accept a Templeton Cambridge journalism fellowship in science and religion a few years ago, a scheme to which I continue as an adviser. At risk of sounding like Richard Dawkins, I don't think I have the belief gene. But I do have a double dose of hope, and that draws me towards the mystical non-dualistic traditions that seem, to me, to underlie many of the world's religions. Despite not being an expert in theology, I'll come back to that briefly later.

First, though, I want to share with you a whistle-stop tour of some of the key issues of climate change and the future of our planet from the perspective of a journalist. Thanks to Nick Owens, Director of the British Antarctic Survey, and his predecessor Chris Rapley, I spent five of the most amazing weeks of my life in early 2009 in Antarctica, reporting on research into global change.

Key issues and debates on climate change

Climate change is undoubtedly the defining challenge of the twenty-first century. What we do about it over the next very few decades could determine the quality of life and even the very survival of future generations. I know that may sound like yet another sensational, shock-horror example of journalistic hyperbole, but almost all the scientific evidence would seem to support it. Next to climate change, history will remember the credit crunch as little more than a briefly fashionable breakfast cereal! So let me give you a little background to how we view our planet.

Way back in 1948, when space flight was still a dream and senior scientists likened it to 'shooting at the Moon' or called it 'utter bilge', the astronomer Fred Hoyle made a profound observation: 'Once a photograph of the Earth, taken from the outside, is available . . . a new idea as powerful as any in history will be let loose.' In just a decade, his prediction came true.

The photo image of the Earth taken during the Apollo mission is now iconic and has, I believe, profoundly contributed to our ecological world view today. It has transformed science, not only through the global observations that are now possible from space, but through the interdisciplinary, joined-up thinking of systems science and the recognition of the complexity and interdependence of the natural world.

This image has also transformed just about every astronaut to have seen it at first hand, and often in a deeply spiritual way. Although I am too young to have been able to report as a journalist on the Apollo missions, I have managed to interview several Apollo astronauts as well as quite a few who have flown on the space shuttle. Every one of them has been moved by the fragile beauty of our planet. It is actually a Russian cosmonaut, Alexei Leonov, who I will quote: 'The Earth was small, light blue and so touchingly alone; our home that must be defended like a holy relic.'

We would do well to hold that vision in mind as we go about our daily lives, turning up the thermostat, driving down to the supermarket, stocking up on Peruvian asparagus, booking that next long-haul holiday and leaving the TV on standby. It's perhaps worth imagining that we're setting out on a trip to Mars. We must take everything we need, from the food we eat and the clothes we wear to the water we drink and the air we breathe. And it's going to be a long journey. We can't carry everything so we must recycle our air and water, grow our own food and make our own repairs. In fact we are already on Spaceship Earth, along with six and a half billion other passengers, and we are totally dependent on our vessel for all the essentials of life.

By the time I got started in journalism, people were already talking about the environment, though mostly in a fairly local or regional way. My first big environment conference was about acid rain and featured an excursion in which hundreds of delegates were bussed into the Black Forest. We looked on with concerned expressions as a few dead trees were pointed out to us. Soon after that, spectroscopic studies by Joe Farman and Jonathan Shanklin in Antarctica revealed a hole in the ozone layer so big that satellite surveys hadn't noticed it. (As it happened, Jonathan Shanklin was still working down at the Rothera base in Antarctica launching weather balloons.)

Both acid rain and the ozone hole triggered sensationalist headlines and scare stories in the media, but both problems were comparatively simple to fix. Flue gas desulphurization and a reduction in the use of coal, plus curbs on vehicle emissions, brought about spectacular reductions in acid rain, while alternatives to CFCs, accompanied by legislation under the Montréal Protocol, are beginning to halt the damage to the ozone. Both still have some way to go and both cost money. But they proved that 'techno-fixes' were possible and perhaps they lulled industrial nations into a false sense of security. Way back in the early 1980s I remember interviewing a Swedish scientist about another environmental concern. His name was Bert Bolin and he was getting concerned by the amount of carbon dioxide being released by human activities.

This isn't meant to be a science lesson, but I'll just remind you that carbon dioxide is what is known as a greenhouse gas. It lets sunlight in through the Earth's atmosphere, where it is absorbed by the ground and given out again as heat. But heat radiation is itself absorbed by carbon dioxide so the energy can't get out. The glass of a greenhouse performs a similar function, as do other gases and vapours in the atmosphere such as methane, water vapour and, confusingly, the CFCs that also damage the ozone.

Don't get me wrong, the greenhouse effect is good! Without it, world temperatures would be perhaps 30 °C cooler and our planet would be a lifeless ice world. CO_2 forms the blanket which keeps our planet warm. What is alarming is that carbon dioxide levels are changing. In the late 1950s, a young atmospheric scientist named Dave Keeling wanted an excuse to travel to exotic places. He started measuring the level of carbon dioxide in the atmosphere around the world and in particular near the top of Mauna Loa on the big island of Hawaii, far away from human activity and pollution.

He discovered a regular annual cycle, as if the world's forests and oceans were breathing in and out. But, as the years went by, another very clear trend became apparent. It's beautiful, clear science and the one undisputed piece of evidence in the whole global warming debate. Calculations suggested that, if the trend continued, carbon dioxide levels would double before the middle of the twenty-first century and that that could result in a global warming of two or three degrees – remarkably close to the latest estimates.

But nobody paid much attention. Back in the 1960s and early 1970s nothing seemed to be warming up and there were some of the coldest winters anyone could remember. In fact, in 1972 a group of concerned climate scientists wrote to the US President advising him to prepare for a new ice age. Disaster movies and doom-mongering in the media were widespread. It sounds a bit like today, only then they were talking about ice. And they seemed to be backed up by good science.

Since the 1940s, average global temperatures appeared to have been cooling slightly. Perhaps the carbon dioxide increase was a good thing, delaying the inevitable ice age. We now know that the rise of post-war industry both contributed to global warming and held it in check. This was still the age of coal, and all those smoky chimneys were putting so much soot and so many acid droplets into the atmosphere that they reflected some of the sun's energy, dimming the sunshine on the ground and cooling the temperature. It's ironic that once the chimneys began to get cleaned up, the problem of global warming got worse.

The hot summer of 1976 brought 30 years of cooling to an abrupt end and politicians on both sides of the Atlantic called for urgent reports from their scientists. In the USA, the first reports did not please President Ronald Reagan or the lobbyists from the oil, coal and car industries. He commissioned another report from former weapons scientist Bill Nerenberg, who told him what he wanted to hear – that any change would be small and slow and nothing to worry about. A story is told that a presidential aide asked a climate scientist how long it would be before global warming became a significant problem. About forty years, replied the scientist. 'Remind me in thirty-nine,' said the aide.

But some scientists kept up the pressure, and in 1988 James Hanson of NASA's Goddard Research Centre in New York chose a Congressional hearing to call for more urgent action on climate change. He was well aware of the power of the media, and the microphones and television cameras focused on him. Perhaps as a journalist might, he sensationalized a little, but the message got through and the United Nations set up the International Panel on Climate Change (IPCC), which was charged with the almost impossible job of reaching an international scientific consensus. In the UK, Margaret Thatcher also recognized the seriousness of the situation and set up the Hadley Centre at the Met Office, equipped with the latest computers to model change into the future.

I'm not going to give you a blow-by-blow account of the progress of the great climate debate over the last 20 years. Suffice it to say it has been an interesting time to be a journalist. I've tried to stick to the science, but the politicians have had a field day too.

In 1992 came the Rio Earth Summit, the first of the big international conferences. Even the USA signed the resulting climate convention, which registered concern but made no guarantee of action. The Kyoto Protocol followed in 1997. That gave each nation that signed up to it specific targets for reducing greenhouse gas emissions. But it required nations responsible for at least 55 per cent of global emissions to ratify it before it came into effect. Many say the targets are insufficient to halt global warming, and even so, the Protocol did not come into effect until 2005, following its ratification by Russia. The USA remains the only developed nation not to have ratified the Kyoto Protocol. Its sceptical attitude, at least early on, was reflected by the Global Climate Coalition, formed from major oil, coal and motor companies. The Global Climate Coalition has now disbanded but there are still plenty of people and organizations out there trying to seed doubt over climate change and urging inaction until yet more data accumulates.

There have been some moves towards acceptance and even compliance in the USA. Several states, including California, have set themselves stricter limits than the country as a whole. And, in the Republican heartland, several Christian groups have started lobbying the federal government to take more care of God's planet.

The effect of climate change in Antarctica

All the climate models show quite clearly that regions warm at different rates. Polar regions show the greatest rises and the biggest consequences. And the changes are not all in the future. During my five-week voyage along the Antarctic peninsula aboard HMS *Endurance* in February 2009 I saw some spectacular examples. This region has already warmed by about 2.5 °C in the last 50 years, five times the global average. One of the scientists I was with, Dr Rob Mulvaney of the British Antarctic Survey, has been coming here, to James Ross Island near the tip of the peninsula, for 15 years. The first time he came, it was impossible to sail close to the island and his ship became trapped in ice. Today there is open water and the boat brought us close enough to the summit of Mount Haddington, where he was drilling and taking ice cores, for the helicopter trip from ship to shore to take just 20 minutes.

Prior to 2002, with good binoculars, you would have seen the Larsen B ice shelf from the top of Mount Haddington. In 2002, it broke up over just a few weeks.

One of the purposes of the 364-metre ice core Rob was drilling from the glacier on Mount Haddington was to see if there have been any other breakups such as this since the last ice age, 12,000 years ago. His ice core gives him a climate record back through probably 35,000 years. By measuring the amount of sea salt in the ice he can tell how close it was to open water at any time in the past.

Our voyage took us much further south, down the western side of the peninsula. The further south we got, the bigger the icebergs became, some of them huge tabular bergs that had broken off from ice shelves 100 metres or more thick. (Remember, nine-tenths of the ice is below the water.) We passed whales and seals and an unexpected group of Emperor penguins. Eventually, we reached the Ronne entrance, about as far south as it is possible to sail in this region. In fact, I think we got further south than anyone has before. By superimposing our course on an old chart of the region, we were able to show that we had sailed nine nautical miles into the ice shelf, but of course the ice shelf had retreated since the chart was made only a few years earlier. Only a few weeks later, a reconnaissance flight returned pictures of another ice shelf nearby, the Wilkins ice shelf, in the early stages of a major breakup.

Of course an ice shelf breakup is of floating ice, like that in the Arctic Ocean, so it doesn't have a direct effect on sea level. At the end of the summer in the northern hemisphere, the Arctic is the focus of news, with clear water evident through the Northwest Passage and sometimes even at the North Pole itself. It doesn't look as if quite as much has melted in 2009, but 2008 saw the least ice there has ever been since records began. What's causing even greater concern are the ice sheets which lie on land. The ice of Greenland is melting at an alarming rate. The past 15 years have seen a rise of about five centimetres in the average sea level, partly due to melting ice and partly simply due to the expansion of water in the oceans as they warm. But that's nothing compared with what could happen.

Ninety per cent of the world's ice lies in Antarctica. Cold circum-polar currents have kept the whole continent in the deep-freeze probably for 40 million years. Snow has fallen and accumulated inland, slowly flowing in huge glaciers towards the sea where it breaks off as icebergs.

The bluest bergs are the oldest; all the air has been pressed out of them so that they are translucent. As long as the balance between snowfall and iceberg production is maintained, all is well, but at the Rothera Research Station we met scientists who had just returned from three months' camping on one of the most remote glaciers in the world.

The Pine Island Glacier, the largest in Antarctica, is the size of Texas. It had only been visited once before, during International Geophysical Year in 1957–8. This time, Julian Scott and Rob Bingham spent three months and a day camping in tents very similar to those used by Captain Scott and his team a century ago; they drove skidoo to and fro across the ice for hundreds of kilometres, towing radar arrays to probe the ice and setting off explosions to reflect the profile of the rocks beneath. Most interestingly, they placed accurate Ground Based Synthetic Aperture Radar (GBS) sensors on the ice, revealing that its flow is accelerating alarmingly – by 7 per cent in the last season alone.

The surface of the ice is practically featureless. They only saw one very distant mountain in three months. But underneath, a glacier is like a living, moving creature. At Rothera, Julian took me down inside a crevasse. From outside you would hardly know it was there – unless you trod on the thin crust over the top and fell in! We had sailed down through a small hole and entered a magical winter wonderland, festooned with icicles. The only light that enters is filtered through ice, giving it an eerie blue colour. You hear a gentle dripping as ice melts and refreezes, and occasional cracks and groans as it adjusts and moves ever onward. Even stranger things must be happening many kilometres down beneath the great ice sheets of Antarctica. There are freshwater lakes down there, some of them isolated for thousands, perhaps millions of years. There are rivers lubricating the base of the ice and sometimes forced to flow uphill by the pressure above. There are even volcanoes. It is possible that the acceleration of the Pine Island Glacier is being lubricated by volcanic activity. But it is also possible that it is being helped by warming ocean currents that undercut it where it reaches the sea.

No one is saying that the entire Pine Island Glacier is going to collapse into the sea – at least not for generations – but that glacier alone contains enough ice to raise world sea level by a quarter of a metre. And if the whole group of glaciers in this part of the western Antarctic ice sheet were to go – and there is evidence that they too are accelerating – it could raise global sea level by a metre and a half, drowning half of Bangladesh and most of the major coastal cities on Earth. That is not meant to be sensationalist jour- nalism. It isn't happening yet and is unlikely to occur this century. But it could happen eventually, and a more modest sea level rise does seem certain.

The other side of the coin is that whatever you say on an uncom- fortable subject such as climate change, however thoroughly you have researched it, there is somebody out there who won't believe it, and they will write or email their complaints. A huge amount of scarce time is taken up in replying to climate change sceptics. Sometimes the reply is comparatively easy, like the person who complained about my coverage of the disappearing ice around James Ross Island. Didn't I know, he asked, that the island is a volcano? Yes I did. But didn't he know that it had not erupted for two million years? Wasn't I aware that it is closer to Argentina than to the interior of Antarctica? Of course. I sailed there. And it was particularly noticeable, on the way back across the notorious Drake Passage, how on one day there were icebergs and sub-zero temperatures and the next we were in balmy sunshine reminiscent of an English summer's day. That's the insulating power of the circumpolar current. But it doesn't detract from the significance of warming to the south.

My television colleague Roger Harrabin had an even harder time when he published this story online. It resulted from an interview with the Secretary General of the World Meteorological Organization and reported, quite correctly, that the La Niña event, bringing warmer water to the western Pacific, had resulted in more rainfall and storms around the world, as a result of which in turn 2008 was slightly cooler than 2007. First, an environmental activist complained that the headline would be misinterpreted by climate change sceptics to mean that global warming was an illusion. More explanation was added and the headline was changed to 'Global Warming Dips This Year'. The title was changed back again shortly afterwards, but not before howls of protests from the climate sceptics, saying that the BBC had given in to pressure from an activist. You can't win!

Climate sceptics in religion and media

It is all very reminiscent of another battleground into which, given that these lectures are supposed to be about theology and public life, I will digress for a moment: evolution and creation. I find it incredible that, in this supposedly scientific age, nearly half the population of the USA choose to believe a fundamentalist religious dogma over and above clear scientific evidence. I refer of course to Young Earth creationists; people who believe, because that is their interpretation of the book of Genesis, that the world is less than 10,000 years old and that humans and all the principal kinds of plants and animals were created separately by God in a perfect world without sin.

Now, I'm not an expert, but as a former geologist I'm impressed by the techniques of geological dating. They appear reliable, consistent and accurate. One of the items in my rock collection is not of this Earth! It's a meteorite. It fell in Argentina in the seventeenth century but it is far older than that. It seems to be rubble left over from the formation of the solar system, similar to grains in meteorites which have been dated with stunning precision to 4,567 million years old, plus or minus half a million years. I guess an omnipotent Creator could have made it 10,000 years ago with its atomic clock hands already well advanced, but by that argument, we could all have been created ten minutes ago. It might have been a lucky escape!

In 2008 I was asked to make a pair of programmes about the debate between evolution and creation. I didn't want to run it in a science slot because, at its heart, it's not about science but about belief and the assumptions that underlie it. It's a similar argument to the one about teaching creationism in school science classes. That's not the place for it and it's unfortunate that *The Times* misquoted Michael Reiss, until recently head of education at the Royal Society, as saying that it *was*, leading to his resignation. What he actually said was that creationism should be discussed in science classes if it was raised by a pupil, so that the class would understand why it is not scientific; not that it should be 'taught' there. Fortunately, in the UK, we have religious education classes – which, I believe, are a much more appropriate venue for a belief-based issue such as this. The USA, pretending to separate church from state, does not have that option in state schools, leading creationists to try to get it into biology classes through the back door disguised as intelligent design. It seems to me incredible that a nation that makes as much fuss about the teaching of religion in its schools as the USA does can allow private universities that are clearly teaching religious dogma to award degrees for subjects such as biology and astronomy. Theology qualifications – fine. But call a spade a spade: this ain't science!

But back to my two radio programmes. I was happy to make them in a religion slot on the World Service but wanted to avoid getting into the rather tedious, long-winded micro-arguments about individual pieces of scientific evidence. So I did away with the idea of a journalist presenter; instead, after much searching, I found two charming people of very different beliefs and took them through a series of recorded encounters with their friends, their opponents and a selection of people in between. They were Eugenie Scott, who directs the Centre for Science Education in Oakland, California, and who is an evolutionary biologist and vocal opponent of creationism, and Henry Morris III, director of the Institute for Creation Research and a Young Earth creationist.

We brought them together for the final sequence on the rim of the Grand Canyon. Had it been a different channel we might have asked listeners to vote on a premium telephone line as to which one would get pushed over the edge. As it turned out, the discussions were very polite but raised some fascinating differences about the assumptions underlying the pair's beliefs. When it came down to it, for Henry Morris, a literal interpretation of Genesis trumped scientific evidence every time. For him, the Grand Canyon symbolized God's anger at the sins of humankind; layers of sediment left by the turbulent waters of Noah's flood. Eugenie quietly pointed out the windblown sediments halfway down, the changing fossil record and the dating techniques implying that here are a billion years of geological history.

The arguments about climate change are not quite so extreme but they are just as vicious, and I note some similarities in the seemingly organized responses I get as a journalist. In the 1990s, each time I made a science programme about evolution, I received letters of complaint from creationists, challenging various details or arguing for equal time to put their case. It was not too difficult to think up equally detailed replies, but it was very time-consuming. In the present decade something very similar is happening. There are challenges from sceptics each time I report on climate change, and it can be fatal to start arguing about the minutiae of their case. Each time I make a carefully reasoned reply, they come back with more challenges, often citing erroneous data as if they were facts.

You might think that the latest report from the IPCC would have enough weight behind it to end the challenges. It has, after all, involved most of the best climate scientists in the world, working with the latest data and modelling them on the most powerful computers. It has even survived the sometimes destructive process of international consensus. Yet the sceptics remain. And they are trying as hard as they can to infiltrate the media.

The worst example of gross distortion, bias and manipulation of the facts in the recent history of factual broadcasting occurred in 2007 on Channel 4. It was a programme entitled *The Great Global Warming Swindle*. The programme put all the main arguments of the climate change sceptics in a completely uncritical way, cherry-picking data that were often incomplete, out of date or discredited. Yet, to anyone who didn't know better, it seemed a carefully crafted documentary of the sort that is sadly lacking on modern television. It was even shortlisted for an award. But anyone who knew the first thing about climate science would have watched it – as I did – with open-mouthed horror.

Let me take you through just a few examples of the arguments the climate sceptics put forward. The first is to deny that there is any warming. A graph taken from *The Great Global Warming Swindle* is typical. It highlights the medieval warm period when there were vineyards in southern England and the living was easy, as well as the little ice age of the seventeenth century when frost fairs were held on the frozen River Thames. But there's no scale, no suggestion as to how the temperatures were derived, and the inaccurately named 'now' point where the graph stops is roughly in the early 1980s, just when global warming was really taking off.

Compare it with the climate scientists' best efforts and there is a huge difference. The famous hockey-stick graph used by Al Gore in his film *An Inconvenient Truth*, which shows a dramatic increase of temperature in the northern hemisphere during the last century, is much maligned by his detractors but nonetheless iconic in climate science circles. Outside Europe, the medieval warm period and the little ice age pass almost unnoticed and the last few decades are significantly warmer than anything before them. If we home in on the last century, the *Great Global Warming Swindle* graph still stops short of the hottest years and draws attention to an apparent cooling between about 1940 and 1970. This is the mark of global dimming caused by all the fine particles emitted by industrial chimneys and temporarily masking the warming.

Another frequent criticism is that cities have expanded and trap heat around them, so that temperature monitoring stations that were once on the outskirts are now surrounded by warm buildings. That can indeed be the case but the IPCC has taken great pains to exclude such data. What's left still records warming at remote stations and at sea. Early measurements from space suggested that warming might not be taking place, but then it was realized that friction at the top of the atmosphere was slowing the satellites, lowering their orbit and biasing their measurements. Those data have long been discredited but still turn up on climate sceptics' web sites.

Another ploy is to say that the warming is real but it's not due to carbon dioxide or human activity. A graph from *The Great Global Warming Swindle* shows an apparent correlation between temperature and solar activity, the theory being that the solar wind blows away cosmic rays from deep space that would otherwise cause cloud formation high in the atmosphere. That is probably a genuine effect but it is tiny, and had the broadcasters bothered to continue the solar data beyond where it conveniently ends in about 1976, they would have seen it fade away in a completely different trend from that of the climate.

Then again, the sceptics suggest that CO_2 levels rise a century or more after the temperature does, and that they result from warming of the oceans rather than causing the warming in the first place. That has probably also been true in the geological past, but this time things are different. Carbon dioxide levels are already higher than they have been at any time in the last 650,000 years, since the ice core record began, and they clearly lead the recent temperature rise.

After considering a 176-page criticism of *The Great Global Warming Swindle*, the broadcasting regulator, Ofcom, found that the programme did not fulfil Channel 4's obligation to be impartial and it also treated interviewees unfairly. But the regulator decided that the film did not mislead audiences 'so as to cause harm or offence'. Ofcom said that it is obliged only to see that news programmes meet 'due accuracy', and that this was not a news programme. Sounds like a licence to put all sorts of fiction into a documentary.

The problem of reductionism in science and dualism in religion

Finally, I would like to put our relationship with our environment into a historical, theological and personal context. Why is it that the world's religions seem to have had so little to say in the climate debate? They play a much more active role in debates about bioethics: stem cells, embryo experiments and so on – they don't always express views with which I agree, but that's another matter. Religions – or at least the Christian denominations – have plenty to say on poverty and consequently on sustainability. But they often seem to stop short of linking these with climate. Yet it's for climate reasons as well as political ones that a billion people lack a clean water supply and hundreds of millions suffer malnutrition. It is climate change that threatens the poorest people the most and, ironically, it's CO_2-generating affluence to which many of them aspire.

So why haven't religion and science managed to engage with the subject in a more meaningful way? I blame Galileo and the nature of the Western mind. Galileo wanted to put clear water between the scientific things he studied with his telescope and other measuring devices and the ethical and spiritual matters of the Church, so he divided the world into the objective, 'primary' qualities that could be measured and the internal or 'secondary' qualities of thoughts and experiences. Descartes said much the same, giving the extended measurable things, the *res extensa*, to science and the knowing things of the soul, the *res cogitans*, to the Church.

It is this Cartesian divide that has coloured science ever since. It persists, within the minds of many individual scientists who also hold Christian beliefs, as what the late Harvard biologist Stephen J. Gould rather pompously called non-overlapping magisteria. Personally I prefer a rather more Eastern representation!

But why do we persist with this 400-year-old dichotomy of convenience? It's no longer out of fear of the Inquisition. More likely, I think, it's down to the way the Western mind is wired. We, or at least most academics, have highly analytical minds. We like to separate things into their smallest components, give them names and put them in boxes. In short, we are wired for reductionism.

It's a bias that has served science well and given us the technology on which our civilization depends. But it has also limited science and means that we have come late and rather haltingly to ideas such as complexity, holism and emergence. It could be why science has yet to discover, or even to admit the possibility of, mind extending beyond the body, or love and consciousness pervading the universe.

But in religion it has given us dualism. I don't suppose anyone would admit to sharing the Sunday school cartoon representation of God as an old man with a long white beard, but it's hard not to think of God as in some way external to the universe. Perhaps not operating his 'smite' button, but still sitting back as a separate entity somewhere outside space and time, perhaps tweaking things here and there and answering prayers on Sunday. He is essentially an external God, made personal to those who believe in him through relationship rather than through oneness.

A few years ago I went to a myth interpretation workshop in Greece run by a wonderful man named Emilios Bouratinos. We picked a favourite myth and began, first in silence then through dialogue, to explore what it might mean to us. I chose the story of Adam and Eve. It seemed to me to be an allegory for the development of the modern human mind. For me, the fruit of the tree of knowledge was what gave us language. Language gives us a certain power over all other life and the ability to accumulate knowledge as a society.

But it also brings about a separation from the bliss of unity in Paradise. Once we can give things names we can separate them from ourselves and from each other. I am this, that is that, I am not that. I am not part of God. Perhaps it is this sense of separation that defines the suffering of the human condition. Perhaps that is why the Bible, at its most mystical moments, refers to God simply as *I am*.

An integral approach to climate change

But enough of my trumped-up theology. Let me end with a brief passage that I think sums up how I feel, or at least would like to feel, and how we can be one with our environment, atmosphere and all. It actually comes from a teacher of the Vedic tradition in India, Shantanand Saraswati, from whom I learned meditation, but I think it resonates very well with us all. It's about discovering our true selves:

> If you begin to be what you are, you will realize everything, but to begin to be what you are, you must come out of what you are not. You are not those thoughts which are turning, turning in your mind. You are not those changing feelings. You are not the different decisions you make and the different wills you have. You are not that separate ego. Well then, what are you? You will find when you have come out of what you are not, that the ripple on the water is whispering to you, 'I am that', the birds in the trees are singing to you, 'I am that', the Moon and the stars are shining beacons to you, 'I am that'. You are in everything in the world and everything in the world is reflected in you, and at the same time you are that everything.[1]

5

Disturbing the present*

JOHN SAUVEN

A friend wrote in a letter to me at New Year 2009 that 'Today is arguably the first day of the most important year in human history.' And
I agreed. The reason for this is the unique nature of climate change
as a human problem that will be dealt with at Copenhagen by the
world's political leaders at the end of 2009. We know that dangerous
climate change is a threat to our 'civilization'. We know from our
scientists that greenhouse gas emissions must be moving downwards
globally within the next 100 months if we are to have any chance of
staying below a 2 °C global rise in temperature. And we know how
hard it is for people to act on that information. They say people
learn from history. What I learn from history is that people do
not learn willingly from the past mistakes of other generations. *We
repeat ourselves.* We are too often content to let the future redeem
the mistakes of the present. It's the very opposite of sustainability –
which is to meet the needs of the present without compromising the
ability of future generations to meet their own needs.

Economic crisis and climate change

The nature of the climate is such that the future cannot redeem
today's mistakes. Once a given concentration of carbon is in the
atmosphere, the change it drives goes on and on, even if it takes
decades or more to fully express itself. In the most literal sense, the
sins of the fathers will indeed be visited on the sons, and well beyond
the third and fourth generation.

We have one chance, and one chance only, to get this problem
right and 2009 is the year in which we take that chance at Copenhagen.
What will history say of us? The events that define the future

---

*This chapter was written before the summit at Copenhagen in December 2009.

57

have not yet happened. What we do this year will determine the outcome.

As President Obama admits, our current ways are irresponsible madness. In his inauguration speech he said:

> That we are in the midst of crisis is now well understood. Our nation is at war, against a far-reaching network of violence and hatred. Our economy is badly weakened, a consequence of greed and irresponsibility on the part of some, but also our collective failure to make hard choices and prepare the nation for a new age. . . . each day brings further evidence that the way we use energy strengthens our adversaries and threatens our planet.

At heart, the world's problems are economic. Economic growth is a means to an end, not an end in itself. But society has forgotten this. To measure the health of our society, our world, we need to know what this economic growth has helped us accomplish, and at what cost. Not just how much motion it has generated and money it has spent.

Every time we talk about 'the global economic downturn', or the need to 'stimulate or kick-start the economy', what we are doing is urging *more* expenditure, *more* motion, without regard either to what its environmental and social consequences are and what it might really accomplish, or to what it might crowd out or displace in the process. The so-called 'health' of the economy includes the billions of dollars spent on war, the billions of dollars on adapting to climate change, the billions of dollars on health care for obesity or any of the other diseases of affluence. And there's another component to the economy: what it does not value. Our economic model, championed these past few decades, has put the value of our joint home, planet earth, at precisely zero. There is no economic value put on our forests, our water, our soil, the life in our oceans or our biosphere, though all these natural capital assets are vital to sustaining life on this planet.

And because we put no economic value on them, we have been looting our home with impunity. The economic model we have created is built on the liquidation of these natural capital assets. In the economic jargon, costs are externalized – we don't pay the real cost. Unstable foundations, you'll agree. For decades, our sub-prime relationship to reality has seen us, as a species, withdraw so much from the earth that our account with the planet is now heavily overdrawn. The environment was never going to be able to take it – it was always destined to crumble under the pressure of unchecked growth. And now we are facing two toxic time bombs – financial and ecological – and they are not unrelated. As our financial debts have built up, so have our debts to nature – registered on nature's ledger as the loss of topsoil, forests, fresh water and biodiversity, and the instability of the global climate.

Increasingly scientists are identifying scarcity of land, water, oil and food – and, especially, 'airspace' for our carbon emissions – as the hallmark of tomorrow's world. Just as a credit crunch was inevitable, so is a climate crunch if business as usual continues. So is a fisheries collapse, and a whole host of other environmental breakdowns. Our leaders are still consumed by the rather naïve belief that we can have infinite economic growth on a finite planet. To a degree, they're right. As the world's ecosystems are diminished, Gross Domestic Product (GDP) often increases. From 1981 to 2005, global GDP more than doubled, in contrast to the 60 per cent of the world's ecosystems currently being degraded in an unsustainable manner. The worse it gets, the more progress we are making.

But what kind of world will that leave us with? A climate-changing world represents a critical threat to our way of life, the environment in which we live and the flora and fauna that surround us. Yet the temptation is to tinker, to stick to what we know, to hope for the best. But when the scientists warn us that we face the collapse of our biosphere, on which our life depends, we need an altogether different response. When the world's leading scientific minds tell us that, to prevent dangerous climate change, global emissions must begin declining within the decade and be slashed by 80 per cent by 2050, they are not merely offering us advice.

And now the financial doctors – Lord (Nicholas) Stern and others – have sat us down to impart a second opinion, and it confirms what the earlier diagnosis said. They say we need a green industrial revolution, and it needs to be sparked immediately. Because environmental collapse is also economic collapse. In November 2008 we got a third opinion, this time from the International Energy Agency, which said that the long-term global temperature is on course to rise by a catastrophic 6 °C unless radical changes are adopted in the way the world produces energy. In March, we got a fourth opinion. The International Scientific Congress on Climate Change released six key messages for the UN Climate Change Conference that will be held in December in Copenhagen. The first message was that climate trends are following worst-case scenarios. The second was that social disruption is likely – given even low-level climate change.

We have no alternative to making changes. If you think the demise of some of our famous banks was scary, wait till you see the full impact of climate change from the retreating glaciers that feed our great rivers in Asia or the melting of the summer Arctic sea ice at the North Pole. A few years ago scientists predicted that the summer Arctic sea ice would all be gone some time towards the end of the century. Now they are saying it could happen in the coming dec-ades – a disturbing 60 years early. We talk about the drama of the first Wall Street-style crash in 80 years. But a summer in the Arctic free of ice, predicted to happen in the coming decades, hasn't occurred for four million years. In fact the Arctic used to be green, but that was 49 million years ago. Earlier in 2009, more than 150 top marine researchers who signed the Monaco Declaration warned that ocean acidification, which they refer to as 'the other CO_2 problem', could make most regions of the ocean inhospitable to coral reefs by 2050, if atmospheric CO_2 levels continue to increase. They also say that it could lead to substantial changes in commercial fish stocks, threaten-ing food security for hundreds of millions of people. Added to this are the big implications for water use from climate change. As the world's population rises by another two billion by 2025 and three billion by 2050, demand for water will rise accordingly. Or maybe a lot more.

It's not just the absolute number of people that makes the biggest difference to water use, but changing habits and diets. Diet matters more than any single factor, because farmers use about three-quarters of the world's water. To grow a kilogram of wheat requires around 1,000 litres of water. But it takes as much as 15,000 litres of water to produce a kilogram of beef.

Our diet in Europe requires about 5,000 litres of water a day. The more vegetarian diets of Africa and Asia require around 2,000 litres of water a day. So the shift from vegetarian diets to meat-based ones has big implications for water. In 1985 Chinese people ate, on average, 20 kilograms of meat; this year, they will eat around 50 kilograms. This difference translates into 3 trillion litres of extra water use – almost as much as total water use in Europe. The fact that many of the 1.4 billion people who now live in severe poverty already face serious ecological debts – in water, soil, and forests – will be exacerbated by the new problems presented by changing consumption patterns, rising wealth and urbanization and climate change.

What is crystal clear is that the world's ecological crisis is not a matter for tomorrow, after the financial crisis of today has been solved. As Ban Ki Moon, the UN Secretary General, has recently noted:

> We are living through two great meltdowns. The credit crunch and the climate crunch. The global financial crisis is most immediate; the more existential is climate change. The urgency of the first is no excuse for neglecting the second. On the contrary, it is an opportunity to kill two birds with one stone. The collision of these two crunches could be a boon.

Even Gordon Brown, the UK Prime Minister, was moved to say in Davos at the beginning of 2009 that:

> If we do not reduce our emissions from their present path – by at least half, globally, by 2050, with a peak in 2020 – we will bring upon ourselves a human and economic catastrophe that will make today's crisis look small. And it will be the poorest and the most vulnerable who will suffer first and greatest.

The urgency of dealing with climate change at the global level

Climate change is not a discrete issue to be addressed apart from all the others. The global economy fundamentally drives climate change, and economic strategies will need to be revised if the climate is ever to be stabilized and if we are to satisfy the human needs that the global economy is ultimately intended to meet.

Multiple systems – security, economic, financial, energy and more – need to be radically overhauled. Until recently, the focus has been on the here and now. This short-termism is today more widely seen as a root cause of the world's economic predicament. It created a fleeting illusion of value-creation by emphasizing immediate goals over long-term strategies. Employees, customers, products and planet earth got lost in the focus on the quarterly profit increase. Shareholder value became the strategy, not the result. Like an athlete using drugs to enhance performance, the global economy used debt and financial engineering to enhance global growth. The current order, including the economic order, is ultimately built to fail.

Conventional wisdom is perhaps now less reverential of this hyper-capitalist model – if anything, it is now considered hopelessly naïve to deny that stripping our shared home of life in order to hold a credit-fuelled consumer bonanza is madness. Politicians applaud the work of economists like Nicholas Stern, who famously characterized climate change as 'the greatest market failure the world has ever seen'. But when it comes to eliminating that market failure, our courage and vision tend to desert us. Up until this point, the general public reaction to these warnings of terminal planetary disease has been to light up another cigarette and say we'll think about it.

Almost 15 years after the world began negotiating the Kyoto Protocol, the levels of greenhouse gases are not only increasing, they are accelerating. A full 20 years after the Brundtland Report alerted the world to the urgency of moving towards sustainable development, the planet's stock of natural resources continues to be depleted and degraded at an alarmingly rapid rate. And many of the targets established in the year 2000 around the Millennium Development Goals will not be met by 2015.

In the words of Mary Robinson, the former president of Ireland and former UN High Commissioner for Human Rights, 'This is tragic and unacceptable because we know what works and what kinds of actions are needed to make faster and more equitable progress.' Prevailing mindsets are still warped by the belief that such a strategy will be too costly, that electorates and consumers will not buy it. It's ironic really. I grew up in a world that spent billions of dollars on building nuclear weapons it hoped never to use. When they became obsolete we threw them away and built even more sophisticated and expensive nuclear weapons which we hoped never to use. We did that for 50 years, and the UK is still doing it. The threat of climate change to the prosperity, security and well-being of everyone on the planet, especially anyone under 40, is far more certain than was the threat of the Cold War going hot. So even though we know what the threat to our species is, the question is whether we have the collective will to remake our economy to stop it. In times of adversity people are sometimes willing to think the otherwise unthinkable. Today's financial crisis is a wake-up call. Years of planet-crushing capitalism need to come to an end. The system is out of tune with ecological reality. If

the credit crunch slows global consumption, it could just be the breathing space we need to tackle CO_2 emissions and figure out how to operate an economy within the ecological constraints of the earth's natural resources. We need urgently to ask what we mean by progress, what we want to achieve from economic growth and development. These words have been used for decades to promote carbon-heavy industrial growth dependent on high resource extraction – a model that is now visibly failing. We need to understand that climate change is a consequence of our failing economic system – an economic system that places no value on the atmosphere, the life in our oceans, the forests, the soil, or indeed the long-term well-being of the majority of the world's people. The solution demands fresh thinking. It requires innovative solutions that take into account the larger challenges we face as a global people. We need a new system where human, social, manufacturing and finance capital exist within the boundaries of natural capital. And just as the world's banks are now rushing to detoxify their portfolios and to rebuild their balance sheets, so the world's governments and businesses must now hasten to rebuild the balance sheet of nature.

Guiding principles for environmental and economic sustainability

There are two guiding principles that seem to me to be self-evident. First, don't use natural resources faster than they can be replenished by the planet. Second, don't deposit wastes faster than they can be absorbed by the biosphere. As Herman Daly, a former World Bank economist, said, business should be a subsidiary of planet earth, not the other way round. So maybe the recent shocks and mayhem in the economic market have come just in time. And we should take note of what Stern said, that it is cheaper to act now rather than suffer the consequences later. So, to create environmental stability and global security, we need to think long term and we need to redefine progress. Just as the Egyptians built pyramids and Europeans built cathedrals to last millennia, we need to start acting as if the future of the planet matters beyond our own short lives.

Part of the solution lies in more innovation. The world needs to develop and disseminate technologies that maximize the production and use of carbon-free energy while minimizing our use of natural resources. We need to dramatically increase the efficiency with which we use carbon-based energy. We need to reduce our energy needs. The opportunities for quick and inexpensive emissions reductions remain vast and mostly untapped. Part of the solution, though, lies in less consumption. The world's climate cannot be saved by technology alone. The way we live will have to change as well – and the longer we wait the greater the upheaval will be. In the USA, the massive increase in the size of homes and vehicles that has marked the past few decades has been a major driver of greenhouse gas emissions and the main reason that US emissions are double those of other industrial countries. We need to reverse the flow of carbon dioxide and other greenhouse gases from the destruction or degradation of the world's forests and agricultural land. We need stronger global institutions. If there was ever a global phenomenon, the climate is it. In fact the climate problem needs to drive political evolution. Our current institutions are not fit for purpose. We need a climate agreement. But it can only succeed if we find a mechanism for sharing the burden of costs and potential discomforts. Per capita fossil fuel CO_2 emissions in the USA are more than 20 times the levels in most of sub-Saharan Africa. Ultimately for our security we need to see humanity as a single vulnerable species rather than a collection of nations locked in pointless and perpetual competition and conflict.

At the end of October 2008 the United Nations Environment Programme (UNEP) launched a Green Economy Initiative aimed at mobilizing and refocusing the global economy towards investments in clean technologies and 'natural' infrastructure such as forests and soils – as the best bet for real growth – in order to combat climate change and trigger an employment boom in the twenty-first century. The Initiative document talked about the need for transformative ideas to be discussed and transformative decisions taken. The alternatives, its authors explained, were more boom and bust cycles, a climate-stressed world and a collapse of fish stocks and forest ecosystems. Take forests as one example. Forests are like vast natural global 'utilities' that for a fraction of the cost of man-made machines store water and carbon, stabilize soils, and help cool the planet to the value of trillions of dollars a year. Yet in our crazy economic system standing forests are given no value. Cut great rainforests like the Amazon down, grow some soya beans to feed our pigs and chickens in Europe and China and all of a sudden value is created. We need to put a value on those standing global 'utilities' before they are lost for ever. And that's why hard cash will still need to be found. We need to pay for these services if we are to protect our planet.

The UNEP report outlined a few ideas on how we could do just that. In the first place, it reminded people that inaction will be far more costly. The Stern Review estimates that climate change could reduce global GDP by at least 5 per cent, and perhaps as much as 20 per cent, by 2050.[1] Second, huge sums continue to flow into fossil fuel extraction and conventional fossil fuel utility projects rather than energy efficiency and renewable energy. The credit crunch aside, the problem is not simply a shortage of capital, but more a matter of where capital is being invested and for what reasons. Third, conventional fossil fuels are also subsidized. Significantly, the annual investment in clean energy technologies is, according to the Stern Review, 'dwarfed by the existing subsidies for fossil fuels worldwide that are estimated at US$150 billion to US$250 billion each year'. Phasing out subsidies for fossil fuels, taxing 'windfall' oil profits, and adopting carbon taxes are among possible sources of revenue for the transition to a sustainable and low-carbon economy. Fourth, the auctioning of pollution allowances (the 'polluter pays' principle – internalizing environmental costs that today are dumped for free into our natural environment) could generate many billions of dollars. Fifth, the issue of investment often boils down to priorities and policy choices. One obvious example is military expenditure. A reduction in these expenditures would also free up large quantities of public money for green investment.

In 2006, global military spending topped $1.2 trillion. In the fiscal year 2008, the USA planned to spend more than $600 billion on its military, almost as much as the rest of the world combined. And, just to put it in perspective, governments have committed over $3 trillion as fiscal stimulus packages and $1 or $2 trillion more to aid struggling banks and other financial institutions. Of the fiscal stimulus packages so far announced, only a tiny percentage could be considered 'green'. It's clear that the transformation to low-carbon prosperity will need to be much faster, more global, and altogether more equitable than anything yet seen in human history. Clearly this is a challenge. As David Miliband, then UK Secretary of State at the

Foreign and Commonwealth Office (FCO) said on 7 May 2008 in a speech to Greenpeace:

> The shift to low carbon represents a wrenching transition in political economy, notions of social justice, and issues of international governance. In other words, this is not just an environmental project. It is a political one. It challenges ideas of national sovereignty. It challenges attachment to free markets – since carbon dependence is the world's greatest market failure. It challenges distrust of collective action. And it challenges us to tackle inequality – or there will be no global deal.

Carbon stabilization and economic development

There is one elephant in the room that I want to touch on before concluding and that is economic growth. Our leaders, in public at least, accept two imperatives – carbon stabilization and continuing economic development. They sometimes talk about it in terms of alleviating poverty in developing countries as well as meeting people's aspirations in developed countries. Therefore they must, as a corollary, accept an absolute duty to increase dramatically the level of 'carbon productivity' in the economy: in other words, more output for far less energy (and natural resources). It is the only way to marry economic growth and emissions reductions (as well as protection of the natural environment). Without a major boost in carbon productivity, stabilizing emissions would require a major drop in our consumer lifestyle for developed countries and the loss of hope for greater prosperity and quality of life through economic development for poor people in developing countries. If you crunch the numbers, you find we need a tenfold increase in carbon productivity by 2050. That will require radical changes in the world economy.

By way of an example, similar labour productivity increases were achieved during and after the Industrial Revolution. These were partly the result of technical innovations such as the steam engine, partly in the way people organized and managed their businesses – like Ford's production line – and partly thanks to government policy and a new regulatory environment that saw the development of things like property rights. In comparison to labour productivity, increasing carbon productivity tenfold in less than 50 years will be one of the greatest tests humankind has ever faced. Or, to put it another way, at the moment humanity generates the equivalent of about 50 billion tonnes of carbon dioxide a year, roughly equal to 8 tonnes for every person on the planet. There is however a huge variation. On average Americans generate about 22 tonnes per person, Europeans 11–14 tonnes and Africans 1–2 tonnes. The target, if there is to be any chance of keeping a global temperature rise below 2 °C, is for humans to generate less than 20 billion tonnes of carbon dioxide by 2050. Since the world's population will have reached nine or ten billion by 2050, this equates to carbon dioxide emissions falling to about 2 tonnes per head. So the average American has to move from generating 22 tonnes to 2 tonnes in around four decades.

In conclusion, I think that ultimately addressing climate change is neither a scientific nor even an economic challenge – it is a human challenge. As humans we are often content to let the future redeem the mistakes of the present. It's the very opposite of sustainability and a luxury we can no longer afford.

- We have less than ten years to start making a significant impact on CO_2 and other greenhouse gas emissions. At the moment capitalism does not tell the ecological truth and it needs to. That means paying the true cost of stuff.
- We need to define what levels of consumption and emissions are sustainable.
- We need fresh approaches to rebalance and restore the health of the whole system. The deregulated financial models and debt-fuelled consumerism of the past two decades have failed to produce lasting value and sustainable prosperity.
- We need a recovery that increases our security for the long term.
- We need to pay the environmental costs of what we use. Natural resources need to be expensive.
- We need to make what we need and build to last. Manufacturing short-lived, disposable goods should in future make no economic sense.
- We need new models of ownership that require businesses to be responsible for the life cycle of a product from cradle to grave.
- And we need to tackle poverty differently so that we deal with equity and fairness. Part of that has to be the acceptance of the fact that there is probably a limit to economic growth. Because there is a limit to nature.

The technological ingenuity that can save us from climate disaster and the increase required in carbon productivity look an awful lot more challenging when you factor in economic growth. It would mean almost complete decarbonization of the economy in the coming decades. The potential for technological improvements, renewable energy, carbon sequestration and ultimately perhaps a hydrogen-based economy is far from being exhausted. But it is a radical transformation in a short timescale, requiring huge investment and resources. *It might be easier just to buy less stuff.* Currently we are doomed if people don't go to the shops and buy more stuff. So it is worth remembering that GDP isn't the only measure of prosperity and quality of life. Health, well-being, the state of the environment are others. These measures are more qualitatively and less quantitatively based.

As the sociologist Anthony Giddens recently said: 'Pondering what form recovery from recession should take must cause us to think seriously about the nature of economic growth itself, at least in the rich countries. It has been known for a long while that, above a certain level of prosperity, growth does not necessarily lead to greater personal and social welfare.' Now is the time to introduce more rounded measures of welfare alongside GDP and give them real political resonance. Now is the time for a sustained and positive critique of consumerism which can be made to count politically. Now is the time to work out how to ensure that recovery does not mean a reversion to the loads-of-money society.

And, as Rowan Williams, the Archbishop of Canterbury, said in describing an ethical economic policy: 'It must involve factoring in to our thoughts about money-making one fundamental thing. We have to recognize that we exist in a world of materially limited resource – which means that environmental exhaustion or degradation has to be taken into account in any assessment of the cost of projects or transactions.'

Not for nothing does the root of the word 'credit' come from the Latin *credere*, meaning 'to believe'. All of a sudden we are hearing words like 'belief', 'trust', 'faith' entering the vocabulary of the business pages of our newspapers. And it is worth remembering that even Adam Smith, author of *The Wealth of Nations*, who is often quoted by free-marketers as the apostle of free trade, never saw the free market as standing alone from non-profit values. He talked about the powerful role of non-profit values like humanity, justice, generosity and public spirit: values that got lost in translation when reinterpreted in the modern era, from Thatcher's 'there is no such thing as society' to Peter Mandelson saying the Labour Party was 'intensely relaxed about people getting filthy rich'. Their statements represent all the hubris surrounding the last three decades of financial capitalism.

We need to remember that the most important things in life – air, water, soil, energy, biodiversity – are the things that keep us alive. The scale of the global economy is approaching the limits of what our planet can cope with. As the oceans are emptied of fish, forests shrink from logging and conversion to agriculture, and levels of greenhouse gases in the atmosphere rise, the environmental and social costs of further growth are likely to intensify until we reach a point at which the price we pay for each unit of extra growth becomes greater than the benefits we gain. Maybe there needs to be a more honest debate within society about the direction people want to travel. What we seek is a green and peaceful world.

6

The concealments of carbon markets and the publicity of love in a time of climate change

MICHAEL S. NORTHCOTT

It was first proposed by John Tyndall in 1859 that greenhouse gases – and especially carbon dioxide – play a role in regulating the diurnal temperature of the earth. In 1938 G. S. Callendar argued that fossil fuel burning was raising atmospheric carbon dioxide and that this had warmed the planet by a degree Fahrenheit. Charles Keeling demonstrated that atmospheric CO_2 from fossil fuels was rising from a data set that he began in the 1950s at the Mauna Loa observatory in Hawaii. Data from thousands of weather stations and satellites indicate that the planet has warmed by an average of 0.8 °C since the Industrial Revolution, and that the rate of warming has increased since the 1950s with the rapid growth in CO_2 pollution. Despite a snowy winter on the eastern seaboard of the United States and in northern Europe, January 2010 was the warmest since satellite temperature records began with land areas in the sub-Arctic region showing a warming of up to 7 °C above the satellite average for the previous three decades. Hence there are bark beetles that were not seen until recently north of the 49th Parallel hastening the demise of 100-year-old trees in Vancouver and Toronto, and beech trees are colonizing the edges of the Arctic Ocean.

Scientific agreement – widespread if not universal – that carbon dioxide pollution could destabilize the climate system led to the inauguration of the United Nations Framework Convention on Climate Change (UNFCCC) in 1992, and it is now ratified by 194 member states of the United Nations. The parties to the Convention acknowledge that 'change in the Earth's climate and its adverse effects are a *common* concern of humankind' (emphasis added); that human activities are 'enhancing the natural greenhouse effect'; that 'the largest share of greenhouse gases originated in developed countries'; that 'the global nature of climate change' requires 'cooperation by all countries' in an 'international response, in accordance with their *common* but differentiated responsibilities' (emphasis again added); and that countries have a 'responsibility to ensure that activities within their jurisdiction or control do not cause damage to the environment of other States'. The Convention expresses a determination 'to protect the climate system for present and future generations' and to stabilize 'greenhouse gas concentrations in the atmosphere at a level that would prevent dangerous anthropogenic interference with the climate system'.[1] In sum, the UNFCCC makes the claim that industrial gases are changing the earth's climate, and that a stable climate is a universal common good whose preservation requires cooperative international mitigating action.

The first international environmental law designed to stimulate preventative or mitigating action was the Kyoto Protocol, which was ratified by 184 parties to the UNFCCC, though not by the USA. This is despite the fact that the USA has parked the largest share of greenhouse gases in the atmosphere and remains the largest present emitter after China. The majority of atmospheric greenhouse gas emissions have been emitted from industrialized nations and the Kyoto Protocol committed 37 of them to mitigation actions, mandating an average per country of 5 per cent reductions in greenhouse gas emissions in the first commitment period from 2008 to 2012. But despite the low target many will not meet it and hence the Protocol is widely seen as a failed treaty.

Many resist the Kyoto Protocol not because its targets are ineffective but because the principle of UN-set emissions targets undermines the economic – and hence political – sovereignty of nation states. This is a criticism most often heard in the Senate of the USA, which voted 99 to 1 under the Clinton–Gore administration against ratifying the Protocol and remains steadfast in opposing any treaty restraining greenhouse gas emissions in the USA. The Senate also opposes the Kyoto Protocol since it does not require developing countries to reduce their own greenhouse gas emissions, and therefore it is said to disadvantage US businesses and employers relative to developing countries. And furthermore, majority opinion in the US Senate is 'climate sceptic' and opposes the scientific argument that climate change is related to human activities.

The Copenhagen conference of 2009 was intended to update the Kyoto Protocol, mandating more robust levels of greenhouse gas reduction in developed countries and drawing developing countries into the process so that growth in emissions would peak before 2020 and then begin to decline. However, fundamental disagreements over matters agreed at previous conferences of the parties – the legitimacy of the Kyoto Protocol, the definition of dangerous climate change as an average warming above 2 °C, the science of anthropogenic climate change, the efficacy of carbon markets – prevented any comprehensive treaty being agreed in Copenhagen. The final plenary agreed to note the existence of a 'Copenhagen Accord', a brief memorandum drawn up by the premiers, or deputies, of the USA, China, India and Brazil, but the Accord is not a legal instrument or treaty.[2]

What many regard as the failure of the Copenhagen conference accompanies the failure of the UNFCCC process, and the Kyoto Protocol, to impact in a detectable way on the geochemical footprint of the global economy on atmospheric greenhouse gases. The Mauna Loa record of the presence of CO_2 in the atmosphere shows an inexorable rise throughout the 18 years of the existence of the UNFCCC, including the first commitment period of the Kyoto Protocol. And consequently, as the scientific briefing to the Copenhagen conference states, 'global carbon dioxide emissions from fossil fuels in 2008 were 40% higher than those in 1990'.[3] The failure of the Kyoto Protocol to restrain global growth in greenhouse gas emissions is in marked contrast to the Montréal Protocol which was signed into law in 1987 and led to restrictions on the use of, and then a global ban on the production of, the principal ozone-depleting chemicals. So effective is the ban that atmospheric concentrations of chlorine began declining in 1997. The annual atmospheric ozone hole over Antarctica and the Southern Ocean has stabilized and will likely begin shrinking by 2023.[4]

The failure of the UNFCCC, as compared to the treaty process that led to the Montréal Protocol, is in part because of the greater complexity involved in regulating fossil fuel production as compared to chlorofluorocarbons. The latter were only made by a small number of companies and the largest of them – Dupont – had already invented an alternative. But the failure also reflects a shift in cultural mores that has corroded belief in the value of cooperative action and shared practices for the achievement of a global common good such as a stable ozone layer or a stable climate. This shift is evident in the reliance of the Kyoto Protocol on market techniques – and in particular Carbon Emissions Trading (CET) – for achieving international mitigation of greenhouse gas pollution.

In essence CET schemes involve the imposition by government of regulatory caps on emissions by greenhouse gas polluters beyond which they are required to purchase permits to pollute. Companies or agencies that pollute below the cap can sell permits to others that pollute above the cap. Permits – effectively corporate carbon offsets – are traded in carbon markets, some of which operate within and some beyond national boundaries. A number of trading schemes are already in operation but the two largest, and with the longest track records, are the Clean Development Mechanism and the European Union Emissions Trading Scheme. Neither scheme has demonstrably reduced global emissions of CO_2, which have been rising at 4 per cent per year since 1990.

Billions of dollars have been invested in inventing and managing new carbon markets but this commitment of resource, and of human ingenuity, is misdirected.[5] Instead of physically reducing carbon emissions through investment in energy conservation, and in technologies such as carbon capture and storage and renewable energy, CET establishes accounting procedures that permit polluting corporations to justify their continuing pollution through the gift to them, or purchase by them, of permits to pollute which are tradeable in the growing number of carbon exchanges around the world. So many carbon permits have been issued in the various carbon schemes by public authorities that the price of carbon per tonne is so low as to provide no incentive to reduce pollution or save energy. Consequently emissions trading merely legitimizes existing levels of corporate pollution through market instruments, and hence many industrialized countries will not meet their Kyoto commitments to physically reduce carbon emissions by 2012; though they will have bought international carbon permits to 'justify' their excess emissions.

The economistic preference for emissions trading over other approaches to carbon regulation and reduction indicates a number of problematic philosophical premises that are not discussed in the economic literature on emissions trading. The first is that any value in the earth's system itself is only fully estimable and realizable when it becomes part of the human economy of making and production and is given a monetary value. Thus if there is a value to the avoided harms that a proportionate reduction in greenhouse gas emissions represents, this value is said to have more *productive* power when it is translated into monetary terms and becomes tradeable against other values. This premise goes back to the political theology of John Locke, for whom values in the earth are not intrinsic but arise from human activities in making the earth fertile and productive.[6] Locke enunciates the first theological justification for the dominance of money values in modern political economy when he proposes that money is the means by which work is preserved from the decay that afflicts the fallen natural order, since it is 'a lasting thing which man may keep without despoiling'.[7]

The Lockean theology of money is of especial significance in the context of an increasingly monetized global order. It was Aristotle who first enunciated the view that money is sterile and that therefore money should not be given 'life' by being lent at interest.[8] This position is central to patristic and scholastic prohibitions against usury and endures until the Reformation. Thus, for Martin Luther, when money has power it endangers the fecundity and fertility of human life, and even of the earth. He argues – and here his argument is troublingly anti-semitic – that the Jews in the Old Testament experienced the loss of the fertility of the land of Palestine, about which the prophets complain, because they had begun to lend money at interest, and taken up other kinds of prohibited behaviours – including idolatry. In so doing they had rendered their culture 'inorganic' and so, Luther argues, the soil of ancient Israel was depleted and could no longer sustain life.[9]

The Old Testament description of idolatry is indicative of the root problem with neoliberal models of political economy. Idols are *things* made with human hands. When things are given undue power over people this is no idle matter; it is not only that power given to idols is power not given to God but that power given to idols becomes malevolent and harms those who ascribe such power to idols. Money which is given power through usury becomes an idol and misshapes human society and the earth. And idolatry in the Old Testament is linked with such proscribed practices as child sacrifice, debt slavery, and abuse of the earth. By analogy the cultural power conferred on mathematically described markets over human affairs – including environmental pollution – becomes instrumental to the sovereignty of markets which malignantly misshape or *pollute* – to use the language of the Hebrew prophets – both society and nature. To put this in onto-theological terms, markets are signifiers that acquire an independent, *idolatrous* existence from what they signify. And over time the signifiers acquire mystifying power so that they become conventions.[10] Markets in money, debt, carbon and consumer goods all fuel the growth in greenhouse gas emissions that are threatening climate stability. These markets signify material sufficiency and sustenance, but they acquire such cultural power that money and consumption become independent activities that bear no relation to the physical needs of people or the physical state of ecosystems. Markets in carbon are idols that legitimize the continuation of a consumptive industrial economy and the continuing sacrifice of the common goods of a stable climate and a liveable earth for future generations. In this perspective, naming and resisting the spiritual disease of idolatry becomes the crucial public work of the Church, and of theologians, in relation to climate change.[11]

The second philosophical premise involved in the advocacy of Carbon Emissions Trading as the principal instrument for mitigating climate change is a preference for a utilitarian ethic in which good and bad actions are set in a calculus of consequences which are collectively aggregated. The focus in such calculi is entirely on theoretical end states, since those who perform such sums as a means of judging between different courses of action cannot know in advance the actual end state.

Alternatives to utilitarian and consequentialist approaches to the good include agent-centred or virtue theory, and act-centred, command-ethics approaches also known as deontological approaches. In the former an action and its consequences may only be judged good or bad by reference to the character of the agent who performs it. In the latter an action may be judged good or bad on the basis of the action itself. The recognition of the rightness or wrongness of kinds of agency and kinds of acts in relation to the environment as preceding human aggregation of environmental goods into useable products and services reflects a different moral frame from the utilitarian calculus. In perhaps the most famous enunciation of this position, Aldo Leopold argues that 'a thing is right when it tends to preserve the integrity, stability, and beauty of the biotic community. It is wrong when it tends otherwise.'[12]

This approach recalls the classical and medieval natural law tradition, in which the extent of human interference in the natural order was understood to be limited by the creaturely dependence of human beings on the natural order.[13] That there is relative stability in the natural order is seen by Aristotle and Aquinas as evidential of certain natural laws that are set into the structure of being by a divine and provident creator. This gives to natural order both a physical and a moral force in human affairs, and in the understanding of the nature of the human good, and constrains human interference in natural systems.[14] The utilitarian perspective is part of a distinctively modern turn in the conception of the moral frame which is understood as constructed by humans in contradistinction to the natural order. This turns moral reasoning inwards upon the specifically human construction of values that Charles Taylor characterizes as the 'turn to the self'.[15] For many environmental philosophers it is this anthropocentric turn in modern ethics which is at the root of the larger ecological crisis. For the environmental philosophers Arne Naess and Holmes Rolston, the recovery of respect for nature requires ways of estimating interest and value that do not treat of other creatures as merely finding value in human cognition but as having intrinsic interests and values that frame human agency and actions.[16] In this approach human agency in the world is shaped by biology as well as culture.

The third and related premise on which neoliberalism requires critique and resistance concerns the neoliberal description of human agency. In rational choice theory, individual consumers and producers act rationally when they behave autonomously and seek to maximize their own preferences or interests. This account of human action is not just a description. As an idolatrous signifier it acquires cultural power through its adoption in what Bruno Latour and Michel Callon call actor-networks.[17] The extension of markets into new areas of social life, including environmental protection, trains people and organizations in the pursuit of private property rights and private goods instead of cooperative practices and the shared pursuit of common goods. As Stanley Hauerwas argues, recognition of the common good by individual moral agents requires training in cooperative practices such as those involved in playing orchestral music or running a youth club. The key in such practices is a politics in which individuals recognize 'how their own particular goods contribute to the common good', for actors in such practices experience a sense of connection 'between their own ends and purposes and the flourishing of their political society'.[18] Such practices of necessity are local in character and will need some measure of protection from impersonal and global market forces if they are to be sustained. This is because, as Alasdair MacIntyre argues, cooperative action for the common good requires that it is conducted on 'a scale in which questions put to those who hold political office make possible a deliberative debate from which no one from whom something might be learned is excluded'.[19]

Carbon markets operate on a global scale and involve the creation of several levels of concealment between market actors, such that the 'black box' of the carbon market trade reveals no real information about efforts to conserve energy or reduce reliance on fossil fuels. And, added to the concealing black box in which burned and saved carbon are made equivalent, is the suppression of local knowledge of, and hence power over, energy, forest and land resources where these markets are operative. Tribal peoples who manage their forest habitats through common property practices lose knowledge and power over their forests when they are drawn into carbon emissions trading schemes, such as Reducing Emissions from Deforestation and Forest Degradation (REDD) in developing countries, in which corporately owned plantations are considered tradeable and attract carbon credits while old growth forests lived in sustainably by indigenous peoples do not.[20]

Against the utilitarian and rational choice preference for market aggregates and algorithms such as the black box of the carbon market, Elinor Ostrom in her Nobel Prize-winning work on the governance of the commons describes an impressive array of practices and institutions that traditional communities have evolved for the sharing of common resources such as forests, fishing grounds, grazing lands and water catchments.[21] Individual moral agency is enhanced, not diminished, when people negotiate and work together in face-to-face communities to manage rights of use for the common good. That an agential approach to valuing ecological goods is superior to the black box approach is also indicated by a cross-national study of compliance with international environmental treaties. It reveals that in those domains which have the most active civil societies, the largest number of NGOs, and the most politically engaged citizenry, governments both ratify more international environmental treaties and achieve a higher level of compliance.[22] And hence we may infer that compliance with and respect for environmental goods as internationally defined is not just procedural, as economists propose, but agential, and the economistic argument that CET is more effective because it has a lower procedural cost is invalid. CET is a set of mechanistic procedures that promise to deliver pollution reduction without requiring that corporations, cities, local communities and householders actively cooperate together to care for the climate by reducing their use of energy and commissioning renewable sources of power.

The preference for mathematical models and market mechanisms over participatory forms of personal deliberation and engagement in actions towards a common good such as a stable climate may be traced to the influence of Newtonian physics on neoclassical economists who modelled their mechanistic accounts of human exchange relations, and the valuing procedures of the 'laws' of supply and demand, on nineteenth-century physics.[23] Neoliberal economists, like their nineteenth-century forebears, adopt descriptive metaphors, and construct models of human and monetary behaviours, which rely more on mathematics than on historical studies of empirical human behaviour. Inveigled by the claims that such models provide reliable measurements of, and hence tools for managing, human affairs, governments extend the realm of market technique into more areas of public service provision – including electricity supply – while shrinking participative mediation by the governed or by non-profit non-governmental agencies. The result is that government and local agencies in service provision – from transportation and telecommunications to education and health care – are increasingly marketized and privatized. At the same time government regulation of the banking sector, money markets and private corporations is reduced and economists and bankers have invented an array of extremely complex forms of trade in money, derivatives, futures, debt, spread-bets on stocks and exchange rates, and carbon emissions credits. These complex mathematical techniques conceal the levels of debt and leverage that companies and consumers rely on to pay for goods and services in an increasingly monetized environment. And hence they reduce the transparency of the physical and monetary assets and contractual relationships of which these markets are mathematical abstractions. The effect is to produce what Walter Wriston calls the 'twilight of sovereignty', in which the power of human communities and nation states to order their affairs according to shared deliberation on moral ends, and the common good, is given up to autonomous market instruments based on the movement of bits of mathematical information between computers.[24]

Recovering moral agency in a global neighbourhood

Contemporary globalization links people and places thousands of miles apart in a myriad daily exchanges of goods, including food, drink, clothing and energy resources. The governance of these spatially distant exchange relationships by market technique and money managers conceals the character of these global exchanges. This concealment eviscerates the capacity of individuals and communities in a particular place to deliberate morally and politically on the social and ecological impacts in other places of the material exchanges on which they rely for sustenance and comfort. Climate change is already affecting people on continents other than Europe, and in particular in Africa and Asia, where droughts and floods are reducing the capacity of vulnerable communities to grow food and to find secure shelter. Distant global trades in energy-intensive goods and in fossil fuels themselves, as well as in carbon credits, are part of a global industrial nexus that is polluting the atmosphere and forcing the climate into a warmer phase. This nexus makes neighbours of distant peoples, not by proximity but by the journeys goods and people and pollutants make. If algorithmic governance prevents moral deliberation on these journeys, how might Christians and others recover moral agency in relation to the material exchanges with global neighbours that sustain and so promote the common good of a stable climate?

A journey plays a pivotal role in the parable of the Good Samaritan, in the telling of which Christ is responding to the question from the scribe, 'And who is my neighbour?' (Luke 10.29). The question is a reasonable one and concerns how to judge which moral responsibilities the command to love the neighbour imposes on the individual at any particular moment. Christ's answer suggests that the Samaritan becomes neighbour to the man who is robbed because he meets him on the road in the course of a journey from Jerusalem to

Jericho. The Samaritan and the robbed man do not live in the same street and they are not friends or relatives. But they become proximate, they are put into a relationship of obligation one to the other because they are connected by a journey. The parable indicates that human beings cannot equally love every human being. Only by favouring some above others with moral concern is it possible to rank moral responsibilities and act accordingly, and the conventional principles that inform this ranking are place and proximity. But the mobile material flows, the journeys of goods and services that characterize a modern cosmopolitan life create what Karl Barth called 'near and distant neighbours'.[25] And they require new forms of moral discernment which honour the life of the neighbour who is not proximate to us, whom we may never meet even on a road, but who may suffer the ecological or social impacts of these journeys.

If neighbour relations are created by global trade, then the Christians in Holland and England who inaugurated a new form of moral deliberation over international trade, known as 'fair trade', found a new way to love their global neighbours.[26] Fair trade involves a range of practices designed to ensure that contracts between purchasers in developed countries and producers in developing countries to supply distantly traded tropical goods such as bananas, tea, coffee and chocolate are morally just and not coercive. Assuring that a particular contract to supply a commodity is just in the terms required by fair trade involves careful scrutiny of the social and ecological conditions of each specific product line that carries the Fairtrade logo from field to market. This scrutiny involves face-to-face contact between the purchasing company and the producer, in the course of which the purchaser and the producer put in place working and environmental conditions, and profit-sharing arrangements, to ensure that the product is sustainably and justly produced, and that the fruits of the contract are equitably shared in the community where the product is made.[27]

By ensuring that distant trades are fair and just and do not involve coercive working conditions or ecological destruction, fair trade has raised living standards significantly in those communities in developing countries that have entered into fair trade contracts. But market economists, and state officials, resist the spread of such supply-chain scrutiny into the mainstream of market exchanges because the degree of discernment and face-to-face meeting involved in such exchanges is more costly, and less efficient, than anonymous price allocation mechanisms. Instead they promote an increasingly borderless and deregulated international trading regime, governed by the World Trade Organization, which disallows member states from discriminating against goods whose production is characterized by coercive exploitation of workers or by ecological destruction.[28]

Fair trade is a work of love in which charity is added to economic relations, transforming potentially coercive or ecologically destructive relationships into relationships where humanity and the earth are loved as neighbourhood. The publicity given to this work of love, which has extended far beyond its ecclesial roots, can inform co-operative international efforts to mitigate climate change and aid those worst affected by the natural disasters it brings in its train. The internationally connected cooperatives of producers and consumers who began the fair trade movement are an important exemplar of the kind of ethical and participative network that is needed for the complex international project of reducing greenhouse gas emissions and so protecting the climate. Climate change mitigation requires the same detailed attention by active citizens, as producers and consumers, to the ethics of fossil fuel extraction and use, and to the other sources of greenhouse gas emissions – such as deforestation, agricultural animals, cement factories – that must be addressed by any comprehensive effort to mitigate climate change. And climate change mitigation requires the same effort to practise justice in the relations between developed and developing world, since the 'moral storm' of climate change is that while the developed world's historic and ongoing emissions remain the principal drivers of changes in climate, it is the developing world that is suffering, and will suffer, the worst effects of climate change over the next 50 years and beyond.

Despite the failure of the UNFCCC to date to achieve it, an effective environmental treaty mandating the reduced extraction and use of fossil fuels remains the desirable outcome of the international negotiating process it has set in train. But it is doubtful that local communities, corporations and agencies, and the nations they constitute, will accede to the behaviours and practices of climate care that an effective climate treaty will require without the shared recognition by significant numbers of individuals and communities within each nation that, though distant in time and space, the victims of greenhouse gas pollution have a moral claim on them and they have a duty to love them as neighbours.

Some will question the realism of the suggestion that love and not law can be the motive behind an international response to climate change. Archbishop Rowan Williams, in his sermon during the Copenhagen conference to a congregation which included the Queen of Denmark, ambassadors and international delegates to the conference, argued that it could when he preached on 1 John 4.18, 'perfect love casts out fear': 'The deepest religious basis for our commitment to the environment in which God has placed us is this recognition that we are called to be, and are enabled to be, the place where God's love for the world comes through.'[29]

The basis of Christian confidence in loving action towards creation is that it mirrors the love of God revealed in the original goodness of creation. Whereas the negative emotion of fear – such as that provoked by apocalyptic accounts of ecological disaster – is unlikely to motivate the changes in lifestyle that the ecological crisis requires, 'the truth is that what is most likely to get us to take the right decisions for our global future is love', and not only love of neighbour but love of God's creation, of the 'world we inhabit'.[30]

This account of love as the spiritual root of moral transformation resonates with an Orthodox account of Christian ethics in which good work and acts of virtue find their meaning and purpose when they 'manifest God' and reveal the divine image in the actor.[31] As the fourth-century desert father St Makarios put it, 'It is in the renewal of the intellect, in the peace of our reasonings, and in love and heavenly eros for the Lord that the new creation of Christians is distinguished from all other men of the world. This was why the Lord's coming took place.'[32]

In Orthodox theology the human heart is a microcosm of the whole cosmos, and of the transforming presence of the Church within it, and works of charity and mercy are the form of the restoration of creation which begins in the lives of the saints. As Isaac the Syrian puts it, 'What is a merciful heart? A heart which burns for all creation, for men and birds and animals and demons, for every creature.'[33]

The moral force of acts of religious charity is understood by political scientists as a form of 'social capital' which represents a 'resource' for generating social trust and the 'production' of the common good in society.[34] The collective form of this social capital, according to Corwin Smidt, is the 'network of social friendships and reciprocity' through which churches, and parachurch organizations, build forms of diakonic outreach in society. But this instrumentalist and utilitarian description misses the spiritual character of charity and ecclesial community, and the spiritual origin of works of love in the love of God and in the love of God's creatures.

Churches and Christian environmental organizations around the world are demonstrating their love for God and creation in shared and networked actions to mitigate their own climate impacts by commissioning renewable electricity generation, and sharing alms with those, particularly in the developing world, who are already suffering from climate change. Lutheran churches in Germany and Switzerland have put solar panels on south-facing church roofs and used the money saved from their energy bills to sponsor renewable power in churches in Africa. The Christian environmental organization Interfaith Power and Light in the USA has contracted to supply renewable supply to churches, and to the power grid, in more than 30 states across the Union while at the same time educating church members in energy conservation and home insulation and in lower carbon living, including transportation and diet. In the UK the Ecocongregation network is encouraging local churches to connect creation care – and more especially climate care – with Christian worship, as well as with the ecological footprint of the local church and with the homes and lives of their members. And the Church of England has commenced a 'Shrinking the Footprint' project in which every church and diocese seeks not only to reduce its energy consumption and to educate churchgoers in climate care, but also to use funds so saved to support renewable energy projects and climate adaptation projects in the developing world. These works of love do have cultural power, but not like the power of capital. Instead this power emanates from the spiritual challenge the works present as signifiers of true worship which resists the idolatry of market techniques, as manifest in endless consumption and in the neoliberal subversion of international cooperation for the common good of a safe climate.

Kierkegaard, Copenhagen's most famous philosopher, argues in his *Works of Love* that Christianity is the world's greatest philosophy because it makes of love the supreme duty, the 'royal law' of the philosopher king Jesus Christ. No other philosophy – pagan or rationalist – marries love and law, and so turns desire into duty, in this way. By so doing Christianity secures love as humanity's end, for 'only when it is a duty to love, only then is love eternally secure'.[35] Securing a stable climate is a common good that requires acts of love and sacrifice beyond those envisaged by corporate and political leaders in Copenhagen in 2009. The Church remains as a place in which such acts of love are both ascetic disciplines and the Christ-inspired embodiment of true human flourishing. And hence, solar panels on church roofs, bicycles outside Sunday services, Christians who refuse to fly and drive, wind farms commissioned by Christian climate activists are not just examples of ecclesiastical footprint shrinking but the publicity of love in a time of climate change.

7

Exploring a public theology for here on earth

CLIVE PEARSON

Setting an agenda

The very nature of a public theology is to engage with occasional issues which grab the public concern and require immediate and/or long-term attention. The common practice is to argue that the purpose of a public theology is to nurture the public good, a civil society, or the flourishing of all. The debates over climate change fall only too readily into these categories. The future well-being of life as we know it in the ecozoic era – the anticipated era following the present cenozoic period, in which time humans will live in ecological harmony with the earth – is seemingly at stake. Writing in search of hope, Tim Flannery in his study of life, *Here on Earth*, wonders if the 'war against nature' has left us poised at sustainability's 'eleventh hour'.[1] Few other themes can rival the claim that climate change poses for this emerging discipline in terms of its agenda.

The relationship between this theme and a public theology is not without the potential for dispute. The charge is sometimes made that a public theology is on occasions too accommodationist, that it encourages 'the world' to set the agenda for theology rather than the other way round. For that reason Charles Mathewes prefers to speak of a 'theology of public life'. Far too often public theologies 'let the "larger" secular world's self-understanding set the terms, and then ask how religious faith contributes to the purposes of public life'. Mathewes is right to point towards this risk and its corollary: that the primary interlocutors for much public theology are 'non-believers sceptical of the civic propriety of religious engagement in public life'.[2]

The scope for 'the world' to set the agenda through this attention to climate change is almost self-evident. The condition of 'the world', the Earth, Gaia is at stake. Its fragility and resilience press in upon us. It comes as no surprise that a detailed description of the condition of the Earth is often displayed first before there is some theological or ecclesial reference. This strategy is adopted by Seán McDonagh in his *Climate Change*. It is only in his final chapter that the churches' response or otherwise is described. In the meantime he has discussed the atmosphere, extreme weather, the state of the oceans, climate change, Kyoto, nuclear power, renewable energies, peak oil and transport.[3] Edward Echlin refers first to 'climatic dynamics and us' and 'evolution's credit crunch' before he delves into a chapter concerning Jesus' own ecology and the confession of him as Lord.[4]

Following Mathewes' line of argument there is an outstanding imperative to establish a theological reason for this particular episode of engagement. Mathewes himself speaks of the necessity of a 'dogmatics of public life'. What lies hidden away in this call is a tacit recognition of audience and task. It is a stock convention of a public theology to say that this discipline must seek to engage with three audiences: the Church, the academy and the public domain. In order to move in and between these audiences there must be a capacity to engage in the appropriate language for each forum; there is need for a particular kind of bilinguality.

John de Gruchy has rightly assessed the importance of an accessible language as being one of the hallmarks of a good public theological praxis.[5] The temptation, nevertheless, is to settle for a one-way traffic of language and ideas. 'The world' sets the agenda and theological reflection happens as a consequence. There is some merit in that approach; there is always the risk that the life of faith will ignore or come late to matters which it should have been addressing much earlier. Mathewes' word of warning, nevertheless, should also be heeded. It is important for a theological or dogmatic case to be made for attending to items on the agenda of a public theology. The performance of this task can strengthen the link between the theme and how it is grasped back in the life of faith because the bridge is established in and through a biblical or theological conviction.

One of the functions of a public theology is to draw upon the resources of the Christian tradition in order to engage with matters and concerns in the wider social and political arena. It has been recognized that particular doctrines can have a public 'signature', 'relevance' and 'consequence'. There is within the systematic agenda of theology itself an inherent capacity to transcend the confessing community. By way of example a doctrine of creation is more than an article of faith for those who profess their Christian belief. It is a theological claim that embraces the whole of creaturely existence.

Now sometimes this demonstration of relevance and consequence can be rendered in a most explicit manner. Sallie McFague, for instance, has repeatedly made very direct connections between her readings of doctrine and instances of ecological degradation. The environmental concern has been like a lens through which she has viewed Christian doctrine and vice versa.[6] Celia Deane-Drummond's *Eco-theology* shows a particular interest in Christology, the problem of theodicy, the Spirit and eschatology.[7] Ernst Conradie has perceived the critical need for an anthropology that better locates humanity and its vocation in the earth community.[8] Denis Edwards has constructed an eco-theology on the foundations of Christology and a reading of the Trinity.[9] This list could easily be extended. And, now and then, there are articles taken from the field of biblical studies which very directly address matters. With respect to climate change Barbara Rossing, for example, has explored global warming in the light of 2 Peter and Revelation. The hermeneutical bridge is established through the canonical themes of end times, 'the end of empire', the urgency of the present moment, and a time for repentance and public testimony.[10] In a similar vein Michael Northcott has imaginatively woven biblical texts and narratives in a most striking way into his study of climate change and a Christian ethic.[11]

For others the connection may be more inferential, less direct, a little delayed and something into which the recipient of such a theology grows. Writing in the *International Journal of Public Theology*, Daniel Munteanu, originally from Romania, has composed an environmental theology out of his Orthodox tradition.[12] There is no reference to climate change per se; there is no detailed analysis of ecumenical reports on the condition of the planet; there is no catalogue of extinction. His work resonates with John Zizioulas's lectures delivered at King's College, London on the theme of the preservation of God's creation.[13] Here Zizioulas drew upon a rich Orthodox theology to create an ethos, a canopy under which the human being can become a priest of creation and nature acquires sacrality through its association with what is holy, with God.

It is important for the plausibility of a public theology to set an agenda that respects its audiences. The potential complaint Mathewes has identified of such theologies being too easily subjected to the concerns and discourses of 'the world' must be addressed. It is equally important to converse with other options in faith which might be less receptive to a public theology. There is an issue embedded here which has to do with the inner integrity of the Christian faith as well as its capacity to speak into a public forum which is likely to be bemused by the plurality of Christian witness. The otherworldly and eschatological natures of a Christian profession can look for a new heaven and a new earth where there is no connection with this present age. There is no theological need to be bothered with climate change or the common good at all. The letter columns in denominational newspapers are often littered with a mix of scientific scepticism concerning climate change and theological suspicion. One of the audiences for a public theology is to talk back into the churches and handle the internal debate as well.

It can be helpful in this set of circumstances to recall the case McFague has made for an ecological dimension to theology and Christian discipleship. One of her underlying convictions is that climate change leads to two central questions: who is God? And who are we?[14] That these should now be her core questions is consistent with how she had previously read the doctrine of creation as an article of faith. The point is simple and straightforward enough. McFague had argued that for us not to act runs the risk of creating uncreation and becoming complicit in the reversal of God's good act of creating and sustaining.[15]

By way of example . . .

There is plentiful scope for this theme of climate change and the common good to become the equivalent of a case study once its theological legitimacy is established. For it to perform this kind of task there should be some criteria for evaluation. How does this example of a public theology manifest the theses of good praxis, for example, proposed by de Gruchy, or variations of the same? Can it negotiate the several tasks and audiences? For de Gruchy this means initially thinking of a practice which demonstrates an informed knowledge of public policy and issues, and a way of doing theology which is interdisciplinary in character and is expressed through an appropriate and intertwining method. Its aim is to argue on behalf of values that Christians believe to be important for the common good in a language that is accessible to people outside this tradition. De Gruchy assumes that a public theology must be committed to the reconciliation and restoration of justice, thus giving priority to the perspectives of victims and survivors. With respect to the ecclesial audience it must draw upon the prophetic trajectory of the Bible and seek to demonstrate groundedness in congregational life and of worship, and must nurture spirituality.

This matter of 'the world' setting the agenda can now be approached by a different route. The nature of a public theology is to be inter-disciplinary. That intention is a tacit recognition of the limits of the biblical and theological subjects themselves. There need to be other insights. For a Reformed theology the underlying assumption here is one of a practical commitment to the notion of common grace. It is usually left at an implied level and hidden from view and simply seen as a normal part of academic discourse.

Northcott's chapter in this book on carbon markets and the pub-licity of love – the public nature of love and consideration for one's neighbours, both geographically close and distant – is an example of such a public theology. His narrative is full of climatological, scien-tific, political and economic considerations. The global neoliberal market system in which policy matters to do with climate change are located is described. The public signposts of the Kyoto Protocol and Copenhagen weave their way into this thick description at key points. Northcott's reading of this big picture is a good example of public reason. Its diagnosis does not rely upon any revelatory claim or special religious pleading.

The descriptive task may well be contested in other parts of the public forum but its language and argument in this respect would fall within the case John Rawls has made for public reason. Here social cooperation is made possible through commonly identified 'discursive principles and practical norms'. The rightly ordered society is established on a public reason accessible to all. This way of understanding the public forum plays down the manner in which 'parochial commitments' can inspire and inform the common good. (Now that is a subject fit for its own critical discussion on another occasion.) What Northcott's narrative does do is present the case why climate change should be a matter of grave concern and how the policy debate might be framed in the public sphere. It is expressed in a way which is recognizable to well-informed critics and advocates.

Northcott's bridge into a more explicit public theology is via his use of some ethical perspectives and the work of environmental philosophers. The desire is to move from mathematical models and market mechanisms to 'participatory forms of personal deliberation and engagement in actions towards a common good'. The particular biblical and theological contribution lies initially with a rhetorical reference to idols and idolatry; the argument concludes with a call for the renewal of moral agency in a global neighbourhood through an application of the parable of the Good Samaritan and Karl Barth's nuanced understanding of 'near and distant neighbours'. This public theology is being converted into cooperative action.[16]

Reading the signs of the times

The spirited manner in which Northcott writes exemplifies the vocation of a public theologian as a connected critic. There is a pressing imperative to discern the signs of the times. The occasional nature of a public theology requires this capacity, almost by definition. Were theology to ignore the matter of climate change, would this neglect be culpable? The well-placed John Houghton, at one time co-chair of the Intergovernmental Panel on Climate Change, has declared this threat to have 'become arguably the most talked about issue of our time'.[17] The rhetoric of global warming, rising sea levels, carbon trading schemes, and various timelines and projections point to the present being a *kairos* moment.

That language of *kairos* has an almost instinctive appeal for a public theology. It is a word with classical roots in the art of rhetoric and practical wisdom (or *phronesis*). Its meaning can refer to the opportune moment for a point to be made and how it is then inserted into the course of an argument. In the writings of Isocrates, due attention to the timing of *kairos* is designed to serve the 'public good in multiple arenas of public and private discourse'. Its origins lie inside a notion of responsible citizenship.[18] From a theological perspective *kairos* can also acquire a sense of Providence. Time is no longer simply linear time: it can become the 'right time' in terms of a reading of the divine will.

The current concern over global warming has attracted the language of *kairos*. For Conradie the analogy can be made with other confessional statements theology has made in the past, most notably in his South African experience to apartheid. Now climate change forces upon us 'a moment of truth and opportunity where our collective response will have far-reaching consequences'.[19] What we say and do (and do not do) right now matters. This *kairos* moment, nevertheless, differs significantly from previous confessions Conradie has noted. Its range extends well beyond one region. Its scope is as much spatial as it is one of timing. No place, no site, no habitat is exempt from the complex web of interrelationships that contribute to the making of the problem or experiencing its effects.

One of the most striking examples of this coming together of time and space is the situation facing Tuvalu. For those concerned with the intersection of climate change and rising sea levels these low-lying islands in the Pacific have become an icon. The Tuvaluans are destined to become a nation of environmental refugees. Their future prospects shot to global prominence at the Copenhagen climate conference at the end of 2009. For a brief moment Tuvalu was in the headlines of the world's media because of its proposal that the rise in temperature should be held to no more than 1.5 °C. For the Alliance of Small Island States (AOSIS) this level was their bottom line; it was non-negotiable.[20] The 'Tuvalu Protocol' led to chants and placards of 'Tuvalu is the real [or new] deal', 'Stand with Tuvalu'.[21] For a moment Tuvalu became a global symbol which 'interrupted' the discussions of much larger, much more powerful nations; its representatives 'drove a wedge' between the islands of the Pacific and the Caribbean and developing nations like India and China. Out of necessity Tuvalu has become highly attuned to matters to do with timing on a world stage.

The spatial reach of climate change and its effects is presented in a more sustained way by Northcott. In his *A Moral Climate* he begins with a 'message from the planet' composed while he was immersed in the Tasmanian wilderness; the attention then shifts to the drought-ravaged Murray-Darling Basin. Northcott's global 'odyssey' has its literary point of departure in Australia. There is time to labour the country's record on deforestation and greenhouse gas emissions, as well as its level of dependency upon fossil fuels for energy production and the threats of coral bleaching to the Great Barrier Reef. For Northcott Australia is a 'microcosm for what is happening to planet earth in the present ecological crisis'.[22] It presents a series of tell-tale symptoms of how the 'global market empire' has placed its biopolitical limits under great pressure. In the course of his enquiry Northcott will traverse the earth for the sake of naming causes, origins and consequences. The narrative he tells weaves together the developed and emerging economies that drive this 'empire' with vulnerable locations, such as Tanzania, the Maldives, Greenland, Bangladesh, Kiribati and Tuvalu.

From global flows to paradoxical umbrellas

The temporal and spatial nature of the debates concerning climate change and its likely consequences effectively means that this theme is a theological global flow. That label is most closely associated with the work of Robert Schreiter, whose study on globalization and catholicity led him to identify new forms of 'universal theology'. The common categories of human rights, liberation, feminism – and environmental care – circulate the globe. Here are issues and an accompanying rhetoric which is seemingly ubiquitous. Somehow, in some way, systemic matters are being named by these global flows which possess the potential to affect well-nigh every theological location. For Schreiter 'theologies of ecology' are 'ideally suited' for being described as a global flow. The 'ecological cause' is indeed 'holistic'; it 'addresses issues that affect everyone, and failure to address these issues means catastrophe for all'.[23] Back in 1997 Schreiter did not specify climate change per se. It now represents an intensifying of his earlier naming of environmental care.

This language of global flows and universals must be handled with some care. It can very easily feed into the discourse of the common good and lead to what Conradie has identified as the risk of an uncritical use of umbrella terms. A paradox is apparent here. There may well be a need to aspire to a language of universal and common experience. There is clearly a desire then to identify matters which transcend the confines of a local context and touch upon questions of human dignity and existence itself. And yet our personal and cultural perspectives on the whole are always limited and may be subversive of this universalizing tendency – and, on occasions, rightly so. Talk of the common or public good can then become highly aspirational, skate over legitimate complaint and disguise an internal politics.

Writing on the Oceanic hermeneutics of *talanoa* (telling tales/stories), Jione Havea has raised a concern for a politics of climate change.[24] Now that reference to politics is not unusual in this broader debate. It is often focused on the competing claims of environmental care and the neoliberal market, and which lobby groups are informing political decisions. Havea is looking through a different lens when he asks who is speaking and on whose behalf. The relative innocence of that enquiry is further qualified by the more persistent concern as to who benefits from talk of climate change.

It can be all too easy to appropriate the experience of the most vulnerable. Following a visit to Tuvalu, Mark Hayes proclaimed a global message: 'We are all Tuvaluans.'[25] He had listened to how local people had responded to a particular king tide, to the islands' need for freshwater security, and to the plight of the *pulaka* (taro) farmers. His article in the *Griffith Review* sounded like an act of solidarity – but it is deceptive. No matter how often a footnote reads 'Tuvalu today, the rest of us tomorrow', the discourse is not right. It disguises privilege and injustice. One recent DVD from Tuvalu did not begin at the airport where islanders were taking refuge; the first shots were of the bright lights of Times Square, New York. The intention was to offer up a different kind of icon and demonstrate that the origins of man-made climate change lay in an all-consuming elsewhere: 'Are we not your neighbours? What did we do to deserve this?'

There is a world of difference between Hayes' appropriation of Tuvalu and the dissertational works of locals like Tafue Lusama and Maina Talia. Rather than reportage, here is the authentic voice of the most vulnerable, who will seldom be given the opportunity to speak in the most venerated of theological locations. The thick description of the 'dangerous effects' of rising sea levels is an account now of everyday living. It bears the mark of an authenticity not so readily conveyed by timelines of impending disasters and statistics. The land is faced with being 'recolonized by the sea'; the people's cry is 'we are trapped'. The theological agenda is saturated with questions to do with how the biblical story of Noah is now to be read. Are the 'end times' drawing nigh? Where is salvation to be found? Faced with the prospect of relocation and the fragmentation of culture, Talia asks, 'How can we sing our *Fatele* [a traditional song/dance] in a foreign land?'[26]

The purpose of this example is consistent with Conradie's recognition of how the politics of climate change embraces perpetrators and victims. It also fits within the ambit of de Gruchy's fifth thesis of good praxis. Here priority is assigned to the perspectives of victims and survivors. This mark is governed by a concern for the restoration of justice, but how does this mark work itself out in practice? This qualifying note is certainly problematic for a public theological discourse. Such a distinction is not merely to be found between classes and nations. It is located within the Christian witness itself and raises further questions to do with voice and with audience. Havea's subverting thesis asks, where does storytelling, the *talanoa*, of primarily oral cultures fit within the high-powered politics and economics of climate change as well as the technical expertise of a well-constructed Christian theology and ethics?

Anyone listening?

There is another element to this discussion on voice. The mere naming of a critical threat to the common good evidently cannot be taken for granted. The issue at stake for a public theology could then be conceived as playing its part in ensuring that a matter of such great import maintains a high profile. This vocation is arguably easier said than done. Havea has alluded in passing to one problem. His aside that he is not qualified to speak on the science involved in climate change is not peculiar to him. The interdisciplinary nature of a public theology is one of this emerging discipline's imperatives and assets. The ever-present dilemma is that only a handful of theologians have the necessary interdisciplinary competence and are capable of being able to shape what transpires on a public stage. The dilemma is compounded because of the rather mixed message the Christian faith can release into the public domain on a whole host of issues – not just this one.

Conradie has helpfully addressed the matter of target audiences and the mode of reception. There is a knot of issues here that needs to be disentangled. The first strand gathers around the ambivalent witness of the Christian tradition itself. How plausible is a theological discourse on climate change and the common good likely to be? Paul Santmire has described the overall Christian tradition as being one of an 'ambiguous ecological promise'.[27] The majority practice has been governed by a motif of ascent; it has been inclined towards being otherworldly, or what Norman Habel of the Earth Bible Project has called 'heavenism'.[28] This world has been 'disposable' and lacked an intrinsic value of its own, independent of its being the stage upon which the drama of human salvation is acted out. The more promising ecological motif is a minority tradition.

What does this history imply for a theological reading of global warming? Is it not compromised by the Christian faith being guilty by association with those Western countries which, Conradie reminds us, have a 'proportionally high per capita emission of greenhouse gases'? Has this faith actually done sufficient in the immediate past to inhibit or warn against the possibility of ecological degradation? Has it not been used to legitimize the exploitation of the earth and a sense of alienation from creation? This style of question is legitimate in the public arena. Conradie is rightly sensitive to how a public theological discourse on the environment is heard. It is one thing to call for an ecological reformation of the Christian tradition and for the ecumenical Church to make pronouncements on eco-justice and global warming. It is altogether another matter for these statements to be heard and accorded status.

There is a point of integrity here. The first mark of a public theological praxis proposed by de Gruchy is concerned with a 'witness to values' which Christians believe make for the common good. De Gruchy is here seeking to resist the temptation to give Christianity preference in the public debate. The practice of a public theology is designed to rely on the quality of debate and the capacity to persuade rather than fall back on some revelatory or dogmatic override. How a public theology is expressed and mediated is as important as what its practitioners seek to say. One of the attendant difficulties Conradie highlights is 'the many conflicts that characterize the Christian tradition'. There is no one Christian position on the environment. It is evident that there is a necessary internal debate within the life of a Christian public theological discourse.

Competing public issues

The discussion on voice is linked into maintaining a profile for the issue at stake. What sets this particular discourse on climate change and the common good apart from those other issues and global flows is the extent to which it calls into question our existence. Conradie has rightly noted that 'we' must always define who and what we mean when this communal language of the 'we' and 'our' is employed.[29] Here 'our existence' is not merely the existence of the human species; already the levels of biodiversity have been seriously compromised. This 'our' is creaturely existence itself. The gravity of the situation is captured by reference here and there to perilous times, ecocide and the prospect of the end of the ecozoic era.

Writing out of Australia, Clive Hamilton presents a particularly grim reading in his *Requiem for a Species*. It is 'just too hard' for human beings to face up to climate change and its complicity. 'Our strange obsessions, our hubris, and our penchant for avoiding the hard facts' have led us to live in denial. It is Hamilton's conviction that it is now 'too late' for humankind to do anything other than mitigate the worst effects of climate change.[30] Michael Novacek's *Terra* is a little more reassuring than Hamilton, who now finds himself dismissed in some quarters as a doomsayer. Novacek is a palaeontologist with a thorough, field-based knowledge of environmental and evolutionary biology. There is still, according to Novacek, time to understand and prevent today's 'mass extinction event'.[31]

This line of argument must of necessity privilege climate change and its associated hazards. But this does not mean that 'items' like the concern for justice, the well-being of cities, the menace of terrorism are unimportant by comparison. It is an invidious task to begin ranking public issues in that fashion. It can also be misleading, because lines of interrelationship can readily be discerned between climate change and other pressing issues. The Earth Charter, co-written by Leonardo Boff, weaves together a concern for the 'overburdened and ecological systems'. The 'universal responsibility' to 'respect and care for the community of life' is placed alongside the imperative to 'build democratic societies that are just, participatory, sustainable and peaceful'.[32]

This desire not to separate climate change from a set of other social, political and economic 'alarms' of the day is likewise recognized by sceptics. Christopher Booker, who takes strong exception to 'warmists' and is noted for his contrarian points of view on many issues, is a case in point. Booker himself is not a scientific expert in this field. His public role is mediated through his writing as a columnist in the *Sunday Telegraph* and in several books, one of which has been dubbed the 'definitive manual' for climate sceptics.[33] The space Booker occupies in the debate over climate change is consistent with the role assigned to the media by Jürgen Habermas as 'sensors' and 'opinion-makers'. It is a role which cannot be discounted. For Booker the 'panic over man-made global warming' – the 'new secular religion' – is only one of a number of crises which have been exploited to 'scare us to death'.[34] Booker's string of complaints are much more specific to particular incidents like the millennium bug, mad cow disease, passive smoking, the asbestos 'scam' and the rise of 'the health and safety culture'. Here we do not have the big-picture public themes Boff has identified; rather we have a web of fears which have invaded the public space and which Booker and his co-writer, Richard North, believe are all part of a common fearmongering phenomenon. They take their place inside what Scott Bader-Saye has elsewhere described as a culture of fear.[35] For Booker climate change does not stand in isolation from other panics and crises. It exists alongside a range of other issues forever competing for attention in a marketplace of opinions, ideas and political strategies.

The public forum in which this kind of theology for sceptics, the secular religion of climate fears, is to be done is far from stable and settled. It thrives on 'news', the extraordinary, sensation. It is vulnerable and easy to hijack. At the best of times it is not a well-ordered, well-laid-out site. To some extent the prospect of this disorder is already present in the malleable nature of the word 'public' itself. Alastair Hannay has demonstrated how it can refer to matters as diffuse as the profile of a person, a venue, a spirit, an audience, as well as 'things' like holidays, parks, libraries, halls, schools, baths, toilets, houses, and matters like service, spirit, affairs, speech and officials. In terms of the present discussion on climate change and the flourishing of all, the presumption is that the idea of the public presumes a participatory democracy. It implies a 'common', accessible domain or office where it is possible to act, play, hear, speak, debate or be a spectator.[36] Here the public may be subject to tides of opinion and groundswells which can turn in a moment and can easily privilege one cause at the expense of another. This public may be well informed or redneck and reactionary; it may be discerning and perceptive, or wooed, massaged and manipulated.

It is not difficult to find critics of Booker's 'rant' on scaremongering. The case he makes can be dismissed in the responsible media as 'bunk' or 'pure rubbish'. The public theologian might even simply look the other way and ignore all the arguments she or he collates in order to subvert the thesis that the level of global warming has been accelerated through human activity. Is such a posture a mistake? The issue at hand may have less to do with answering each counter case like those Booker provides than with reading effectively how the public landscape is constructed. There is no guarantee that global warming, carbon emissions and rising sea levels can secure a hold on the public mind and maintain constancy.

The experience of Australia is a case in point. The record of the Howard government (1996–2007) on climate change was noted for that government's refusal to sign the Kyoto Protocol. The occasional apologist has cited its deference to 'professional expertise' and the 'advice of high profile scientists and activists'. Jennifer Marohasy, a biologist and member of the think tank the Institute of Public Affairs, listed the programmes designed to arrest soil degradation, enhance biodiversity and promote conservation, but noted that now 'we seem to have been caught up in the drama of an imaginary climate crisis'. She conceded that Howard was more likely to be remembered for the decision on Kyoto.[37] Hamilton's reading of this period is rather different. The Howard years should be seen as being characterized by a web of 'dirty politics'. That reluctance to sign the Kyoto Protocol was a reflection of the influence brought to bear on the politics of climate change by lobbyists, the fossil-fuel industry, a media that 'slumbered' and a government forever poised for a moment of electoral opportunism.[38] The consequence of this strategy was the reversal of a public opinion which had formerly desired Australia to take a lead in sustainable development.

The momentum altered again with Kevin Rudd's victory at the polls. His first official act was to sign the Kyoto Protocol; it was followed within a fortnight by the release of a white paper which set out the plan to launch an emissions trading scheme by 2010. *The Garnaut Climate Change Review* was commissioned to examine the likely effects of climate change on the Australian economy and provide a framework for subsequent mid- to long-term policy.[39] It was evident that, despite criticism of the carbon reduction scheme by Garnaut and other climate activists at home, the Rudd government wished to place Australia at the forefront of the world stage with its acceptance of the need to act now, and decisively, on matters to do with global warming. All of a sudden climate change became the prime concern on commissioned news polls. And yet the volatile and changeable nature of the public sphere is clear. The Emissions Trading Scheme Bill was defeated in the Senate only days before the Copenhagen conference and accord. How to deal with asylum seekers and 'people smugglers' has now replaced climate change in the opinion polls. By Easter 2010 the level of public concern for global warming and related issues had fallen to its lowest in three years. The comparison is with Rudd's expedition to Bali in order to sign the Kyoto Treaty and declare Australia's readiness 'to assume its responsibility'. The claim was made that 'Climate change is the defining issue of our generation.'[40]

On being resilient

It is evident that a public theology must be resilient. The ebb and flow of the public debate on climate change has demonstrated how susceptible it is to competing interpretations and vested interests. The common good is far from straightforward. The public square is a contested place and the Church is likewise seldom of one mind on matters in this domain. It should come as no surprise that one of the virtues so often espoused with regard to a public theology is wisdom. There is a need for discernment. The discipline is also by its very nature hopeful. It aspires after what might be and recognizes that this lies in the future. It will require a particular kind of praxis in order to come to fruition.

Peter Scott assumes the messy nature of the public sphere and how there is no agreement over the meaning of climate change. There is due recognition that this umbrella term is not just scientific but also a cultural phenomenon which requires interpretation. Scott posits the importance of a public theology of resistance. The debates over what constitutes climate change may well be daunting and the politics complex. There may well be a need for resilience and its biblical equivalents of steadfastness and patience over a long period of time – but on what basis? For a public theology this stand is grounded in core confession to do with the goodness of God and an affirmation of the goodness of creation.[41] The theological narrative can draw upon its rich resources to offer a discerning word of hope established in the finality of God's goodness and a love of neighbour. Here the nature and purpose of a public theology can come together. What is striking is how close it comes to Flannery's conclusion: 'I am certain of one thing – if we do not strive to love one another and to love our planet as much as we love ourselves then no further human progress is possible here on Earth.'[42]

8

Apocalypse now: Global equity and sustainable living – the preconditions for human survival

CLARE SHORT

I have taken the theme of apocalypse quite deliberately. People accuse those who are worried about the state of our world of talking apocalyptically and spreading gloom and doom, and I think we need to examine that. It is notable, I think, that for much of human history people have thought that they face apocalyptic challenges.

Apocalyptic challenges

The early Christians thought that the world would soon end and Christ would come again to judge the living and the dead, and that the just would go on to live in a paradise on earth. Early Christianity drew on Jewish traditions – Jesus being a Jew – and inherited those traditions. There have been all sorts of apocalyptic movements in most world religions and often they become dominant at times of suffering and despair. They frequently contain an idea that God is punishing us for our misdeeds and that we should return to our true faith, and that God will then rescue us and usher in a long period of justice and peace for all true believers. It was Augustine who got Christianity off the hook of the early Church's belief in the imminent end of the world, which was inherited, as I say, from Jewish thinking. Many Christians had seen the Roman Empire as the Beast of Revelation that dominated the world and persecuted Christians. But then Constantine became a Christian (lots of people think an unhappy sense of hierarchy came into the Christian tradition at that point, but that's another discussion) and Rome became the Church's friend, and thus that idea had to change. After that, when Rome was defeated and destroyed, the old ideas needed updating.

Augustine saw the Church as being the representative of Christ on earth for a thousand years rather than Christ coming to rule for a time of peace and justice, and justice and peace coming to us in heaven rather than on earth. Now since the Enlightenment, pre-French Revolution, we have tended to sneer at such ideas; we believe instead in rationality, democracy, science and progress. But the old millenarian thinking, the idea of a thousand years of peace and justice after the suffering and apocalypse, lingers and has seen an upsurge in recent years. Thus Christian fundamentalists in the USA are yearning for the Rapture, which will transport all true believers up into the sky to meet Jesus and signify the end of the world. This movement sells millions of books and was a significant part of the coalition that brought George Bush to power. It also has very destructive views on the Middle East and helps to incite, I think, the constant breach of international law, making peace between Israel and Palestine more difficult. Christian Zionism has been denounced as heresy by all the main churches, but religious belief and political support for Israel remain prevalent and strong in the USA, and it is stunning to realize that 40 per cent of Americans currently say that they believe the world will end in their lifetime. It's said that Americans are from Mars and Europeans from Venus, and this might be part of the difference.

Such millenarian thinking has a long history in Jewish and Christian tradition, and it emerged in Islamic tradition in the seventh century. It is not in the Qur'an, but in that period it was predicted that the Mahdi would arise in the east, raise an army and march to Iraq, establishing his messianic kingdom there after purifying the Muslim world of evil. Interestingly, Jesus was seen to be part of this. It was believed that Jesus, who of course is a great prophet in the teachings of Islam, would appear prior to the messianic kingdom, slay the Antichrist sent to test the Muslims and then pray behind the Mahdi. And it is perhaps not surprising that some modern Islamist movements have reached back to this tradition. But this deep tradition, that history has meaning and purpose (rather than that we are just living one generation after another) and that after suffering and struggle we will build a world of peace and justice, is not confined to religious thinking. Marxist analysis follows the same tradition. It may be significant, of course, that Marx's father was a Jewish rabbi. And now we have a new secular apocalypse: the end of planet earth.

What I want to argue is that apocalyptic pictures of the possible end of the world, resulting from global warming and other environmental pressures, belong to a very old tradition. They reflect pessimism about the current state of the world, they warn of great destruction unless we build a more sustainable and just world order. I also believe that our present way of life has become decadent – and I use the word decadent deliberately – destructive and unhappy. The challenge is to build a new, more moral, sustainable and generous civilization. But we should remember that the idea of apocalypse was not originally all gloom and doom. The word's meaning has changed in recent times. It was a warning of terrible destruction but it also contained a promise of peace and justice on earth. I believe we need to embrace the risk of apocalypse to recapture hope and energy in order to create the world of justice and peace, which is the only way that we will get the world through the troubles we currently face.

Changing contexts

Now, a little bit of autobiography. I am a child of the 1960s, a baby boomer, and therefore I am part of the luckiest generation that has ever grown up in this country, and probably in any of the member countries of the Organization for Economic Cooperation and Development (OECD). We were born when the suffering of the Second World War was over; we were given free orange juice, the National Health Service, expanding educational opportunities, full employment and a massive change in the life opportunities of women compared with the lives of our mothers and grandmothers. I have always, because of the generation to which I belong, been a deep optimist. I believed, until recently, that if we work hard enough and stand up for what is right then everyone in the world can be given the chances that were given to me and my generation. But in recent years I have come to believe that if we go on as we are, we face a series of tipping points that will lead to mayhem, terrible conflict and suffering, and a possible end to human civilization. It is a controversial argument but it is my sincere conclusion.

We know, of course, that the world will end in three billion years when our sun burns out, but that feels a comfortably long distance away, though if we manage to survive till then it will trouble the people who are around at the time. We know that we, *Homo sapiens*, are only 160,000 years old. We have become too arrogant; the dinosaurs lived for 160 million years, and yet we think they are funny old stupid creatures. We need a little humility. Until 10,000 years or so ago we were hunter-gatherers living in groups and family bands of 25 to 50 people, surviving, hunting, gathering berries, having our children, sitting round talking. We know that other species have ended, from dinosaurs to Neanderthal man. We also know that other civilizations have crumbled – Sumeria, Ancient Greece, Rome and many others. It is quite possible that our civilization will end within a few hundred years. Some human beings may remain, in much diminished numbers, but our civilization could be destroyed. It is not planet earth that is at risk but *Homo sapiens*. We are changing the earth but it will remain, while we may not. This is quite a conclusion for a sixties baby boomer to reach.

What is the evidence? Everyone is aware that development in China, with India following on behind, is shifting the balance of power in the world. Globalization is spreading, as is access to modern technology and capital investment across the world. And in China we have seen more people lifted out of extreme poverty in a shorter time than humanity has ever previously experienced. But these developments are also testing our way of life to destruction. According to Lester Brown of the Earth Policy Institute in Washington DC, whose books I recommend very strongly and who is one of the USA's leading environmental analysts, if growth in China continues at 8 per cent per year or more, as it has now for 15–20 years, then by 2031, China's income per head, for its 1.45 billion people, will be equal to that of the USA today. As Brown has said, 'China's grain consumption will then be two-thirds of the current grain consumption of the entire world. If it consumes oil at the same rate as the US today, the Chinese will be consuming 99 billion barrels a day and the whole world is currently producing 84 billion barrels a day.'[1] And will probably not produce much more – we are certainly somewhere near what is referred to as peak oil, the point at which maximum extraction, refining and production of oil is reached and oil production enters terminal decline. If China consumes paper at the same rate that we do, it will consume twice as much paper as the world is now producing. If the Chinese then have three cars for every four adults, as the USA does today, they will have a fleet of 1.1 billion cars compared to the current world fleet of 800 million. You might think that is a joke, but remember Beijing as a city of bicycles is gone already; it is now a city of cars and SUVs. They would have to pave over an area equivalent to the area that is planted with rice today just to drive and park those cars. Lester Brown has been tracking and documenting the world's major environmental trends for 30 years and his conclusions demonstrate that the Western economic model will not work for China. All they are doing is what we have already done, so you cannot criticize them in any way for that. But what you can say is that it is not going to work, and if it does not work for China by 2031 then it will not work for India, whose speeded-up economic growth is following on behind quite fast (and by 2031 India will have an even larger population), or for the other three billion people in developing countries who all aspire to live as we do.

In some way, therefore, it will not work for the industrialized countries either, because in this incredibly integrated world economy, we all depend on the same oil, the same grain, the same paper, the same forests. The bottom line of this analysis is that we have to develop a new economic model. As Lester Brown says, instead of a fossil-fuel-based, automobile-centred, throwaway economy we will have to have a renewable-energy-based, diversified transport system and comprehensive reuse and recycle economies. If we want civilization to survive, that is what we will have to do; otherwise civilization will collapse. It is useful to stand back and look at the way we live. Of course, my optimistic sixties kid said, 'Everyone in the world should have what we have', but there is not enough capacity in the world for everyone to enjoy the way of life we have enjoyed, though of course people want it. We are starting to hit the crises that come from the complete unsustainability of our model.

Despite our high-tech civilization, we are dependent for our existence on the earth's ecosystems. We are dependent on the climate system for our agriculture, and on the hydrological system for our fresh water. We are dependent on pollination (though even our bees are in trouble), the containment of carbon dioxide sequestered from the atmosphere, soil conservation and so on. Given this, we should be concerned that a recent study by 1,360 scientists titled 'The Millennium Ecosystem Assessment' reported that 15 of 24 primary ecosystem services are being degraded or pushed beyond their limits.[2] For example, three-quarters of oceanic fisheries are being fished beyond their ability to sustain themselves and are in danger of collapse.

Around two billion people in the world depend on fish as their primary source of protein. Twenty per cent of rainforests have been cleared for cattle ranching or soya bean farming. Another 22 per cent have been weakened by logging. The pumping of underground water now exceeds natural recharge in countries containing half the world's people, leaving many without adequate water as wells go dry. Australia is experiencing an advanced version of this situation, and because Australia's economy is so dependent on agriculture they are feeling it very hard, but it is spreading in many other poorer countries.

And during the late summer of 2007 we received news of an acceleration in the melting of polar ice. Mark Sarezze, a veteran Arctic specialist, said that if he had been asked a couple of years ago when the Arctic would lose all its ice, he would have said 2100, or at the earliest 2070, but he now estimates that it will be 2030 – just 22 years away. It is also now clear that the Greenland ice cap is melting much faster than was previously estimated. The same is true of the west Antarctic ice sheet. And, of course, these are above land, so if they melt they will significantly raise the level of the sea, unlike the Arctic ice which is mostly in the sea already. The best scientists tell us that if both melt, sea levels will rise by 39 feet. Something like 80 per cent of the population of the world live in cities by the sea. London cannot manage a sea level rise of 39 feet – just imagine! It was previously projected that such melting would take centuries, giving us plenty of time to reach agreement on reducing carbon dioxide emissions and developing new technologies, but the danger is now accelerating alarmingly and we have much less time to take action.

The same is true of the glaciers that feed the Ganges river in India and the Yellow and Yangtze rivers in China. If those glaciers go the rivers will dry up for part of the year and become seasonal, which would devastate agriculture in these countries, each of which has a population of over a billion. These threats, and the route we are on, would lead to the displacement of hundreds of millions of people and damage very seriously the agricultural productivity of the world. Darfur has already given us an example of the conflict that is likely to follow the growth of population, combined with a shortage of water and degradation of the land. If action is not taken to avert these dangers the future looks very bleak indeed.

Local and global initiatives

But like all apocalyptic visions, painting this picture, which depicts a real threat, undermines the need to create a different future. There are new technologies that can help to make that different future possible. Denmark already gets 20 per cent of its electricity from wind and plans to raise this to 50 per cent. Sixty million Europeans get their residential electricity from wind farms. By the end of 2007, 40 million Chinese homes were receiving hot water from rooftop solar heaters. And in all these figures Britain is right at the end of the queue. In Iceland, 90 per cent of homes depend on geothermal energy, a technology which is useable here as well, not just because special conditions exist in Iceland. Fish farming is growing in China, which is the only country whose farmed output exceeds its oceanic catch. South Korea was once a barren, almost treeless country. It has reforested, checking flooding and soil erosion. Curitiba in Brazil reconstructed its transport system in 1974; since then the population has tripled yet car traffic has declined by 30 per cent. In Amsterdam, 40 per cent of all trips are made by bicycle. The conclusion is that there is much that we can do, but it means we have to create a new world order that is more just and equitable, and a new kind of society that is less materialistic and more sustainable. This is not just a mild preference, this is about us surviving and not hitting a major catastrophe in the relatively near future. The question is whether we can change fast enough to prevent disaster.

It is clear, I think, that people are becoming increasingly concerned about these threats and change is beginning to happen. But it is happening nowhere near fast enough. It is also increasingly clear that the way of life we share in the richer countries, the countries of the OECD that make up 20 per cent of humanity, a way of life to which the rest of humanity aspires, does not make people happy. We have problems of loneliness, mental illness, obesity, drink and drug addiction, and the degradation of sexual love amid stupendous material wealth that would astonish our great-grandparents if they could come back and see us. The world is increasingly unequal and divided. The moral authority of the United Nations and international law is being gravely undermined by the behaviour of wealthy countries and a new kind of warfare is spreading across the world. There is also a real danger of an acceleration of nuclear proliferation. Our own society and the world will become increasingly unequal. Between now and 2040–50, the world's population will rise from just over six billion to nine billion, and 90 per cent of the new people will be born in the poorest countries. Africa faces the worst threats as a result of climate change and has contributed least to its causes.

We have to change the way we live. And if we do it right it could make us happier. These issues are increasingly on the political agenda worldwide but we are in an age of sound-bite, focus-group-led politics. Politicians pick up on public concern through focus groups and feed back to the public promises of what they want, but these are mere words rather than reality. Britain, a country that could be taking up a very useful international role in these matters, lags behind most other European countries in making progress – though our rhetoric, of course, leads the world.

We need to transform the way we live and this change will only come from the bottom up. The Transition Town movement which began in Totnes in Devon is about building local community, local resilience, thinking about what these future threats would mean for the place you live and starting to draw people together. It is spreading fast across Britain and indeed across the world, and it is seeking to build localization and increased local resilience against the coming threats. This is deeply valuable. But the change we need cannot be achieved only by local action. It requires a revolution in the way we live and the way the world is organized.

But massive change has happened before. The street that I grew up in still exists in my former constituency in Birmingham. All the children on that street played together endlessly; they stopped their games only very occasionally when a car was coming. Now, if you go there, there are cars on both sides and no children playing. When I was five, milk and bread were delivered by horse-drawn vehicles and nobody travelled by aeroplane. That may sound like a Hovis advert, but if you think of the change that has happened in the last 50 years or so, it shows that enormous change is possible again. Lester Brown cites the example of how, after the attack on Pearl Harbor, the US economy was rapidly turned round to produce the instruments of war. In fact, when Roosevelt made a big speech about how many aeroplanes were needed, how many tanks and guns, everyone thought, 'Yes, but it's impossible, we can't do that.' When he spoke to the leaders of the car industry they said, 'Yes, Mr President, we'll do what we can', and he said, 'No, you don't understand. You have to stop building cars and we will turn all the industrial capacity of this country over to this new project.' And, of course, they produced enormous resources that came into Europe and helped to bring that war to an end.

In the UK it is worth remembering that, to take forward the fight against Hitler, conscription and rationing were introduced, women began working with skills they had never previously been allowed to acquire, nurseries were opened throughout the country (interestingly, they closed at the end of the war), and because of food shortages and the fair sharing brought about through rationing we produced the healthiest generation of babies the country had ever known. It was a phenomenal change, because everyone agreed we had to do it. The point is not to say let's go back to sackcloth and ashes, although that might match our apocalyptic thoughts, but to remind us of the phenomenal change that is possible if we all want to make it and are capable of cooperating to bring it about.

The urgency of human action

The question is, can we make the changes fast enough? I am afraid my own conclusion is that it will take more catastrophes before there is an adequate sense of urgency. It would require the equivalent of Hurricane Katrina, that destroyed New Orleans, to occur in London and Vancouver and the major cities of the industrialized world, to shake the whole system. Of course, when such things happen in Darfur everybody is sorry, but that is different. Catastrophes will come, but the question is, will they come in ways that enable us to be shaken and changed or will they come in ways that do not lead to change? Because catastrophe can create ugly responses. There is a real danger, I think, that the response will be fascistic. Think of the nastiness that is apparent across Europe now in reaction to 20 million refugees worldwide and imagine how we will respond to the hundreds of millions of refugees displaced by the complete destruction of agriculture. Bangladesh is the least developed country in the world for its size. Its population growth is slowing as more girls go to school and more people have access to contraception, but its population is very young and is therefore going to increase by 50 per cent in the next 30 years. If sea levels rise, it will lose at least a third of its land because it consists largely of a great big river delta. Where are all those people going to go? We are talking about vast numbers. They will go into India, but there isn't space in India. Then what happens? In the case of Africa, migration has been into Europe, something to which there is already a very ugly response. So how would we respond to the displacement of hundreds of millions more people?

I have no doubt that change is coming, but will it be fast enough or ambitious enough? The only way we can survive – and this takes us back to the apocalypse – will be in a more equal, more localized, more just and less greedy world order. Obviously that is morally preferable, but this is purely about the survival of our civilization. If we do not change in that direction we are going to be in desperate trouble. I call these apocalyptic visions; this prospect is a warning of what will happen if we do not change. The point of facing up to this is to create the energy to make the change, to create more justice and peace at home and abroad, and to ensure that we all have the basic material things that we need and access to education and health care across the world. We can do this with the technology and wealth and knowledge we now have. Every single human being in the world could have all the basics and access to education and health care, and then we would have to seek life's happiness in nature, poetry, spirituality, love and community, rather than the constant acquisition of more and more material goods. That is the challenge. I think if we rise to it we can build a better world. But if we don't, it is going to be hell.

Responses to questions

Q: You touched briefly on over-population in the world. China has imposed a one child policy for years, without which they would be in serious trouble now. Is this something that should be considered elsewhere?

No, what China did isn't necessary and isn't right. In fact, a UN conference was held in Cairo in the 1990s on the principles of access to reproductive health care, and the principle agreed by the whole world community was that people have a right to control their fertility and a right to access services, and then to be able to make their own choices. And what we know from the history of the world is that when people's lives get better, and when development brings longer life and fewer children die, you get a big growth in the population. Then, if life is getting better, people have fewer children because they know their children will survive, children are no longer going to work in agriculture, and that is what's called the demographic transition. What we have in Africa is a kind of interrupted demographic transition: there is immunization, some health care, more children are surviving, more people are living longer, but there's no economic development and therefore there's a growing population and growing impoverishment. What we need is to complete the transition in Africa and for Africa to get the economic development and the better life that always lead human beings to choose to reduce the size of their families. If you take the population of the world – I think in 1900 there were about 1.2 billion of us, that was a little more than the number of human beings that have existed since we first evolved, and by 1960 there were three billion. Now there are six billion, and there are going to be nine billion – and we are much greedier, which imposes enormous demands on the resources and capacity of the planet. If we do not attend to this there will be more and more poverty, and the population is also urbanizing so there will be more anger. If you look at what happened in Britain at the time of the Industrial Revolution, the rural poor were more passive than the urban poor. The urban poor can organize politically and riot, and Africa is urbanizing. So we do not need the cruelties of the Chinese one child policy, but we do need universal access to contraception so that people can control their own fertility. And we need to guarantee development to Africa that will bring about the decline in family size that we have seen in all other societies across the world.

Q: Who is letting who down in the move towards trying to cure the problems and avoid or avert apocalypse? Are the scientists and the engineers failing to provide the solutions? Are the politicians failing to produce the leadership and the policies? Or is it the media or religious groups who aren't actually putting the message across as hard and as fast as they might?

I think it is all of us. I think the change that is needed is as big a change as were the Industrial and French Revolutions, the end of feudalism, the beginning of the nation state. The beginning of industrialization was an utter revolution in human history and, of course, it brought belief in democracy and human rights. Marx, that other secular apocalyptic philosopher, saw that industrialization was going to lift humanity despite the ugliness of the factories and thought that, as we used development, everyone in the world would have enough and we would not need repressive governments. That was his vision. But, of course, it left out the strain on the world's environment; otherwise, if you look at China now you could say that, in some fundamental way, he was right. So I think that the global political elite is completely out of touch with the problems of these times. I think they are failing us disgracefully, and it isn't just one or two leaders. It makes you think about the Roman Empire, when everyone was within the reach of that elite but it was all about to crumble – I don't think America is going to crumble that fast, but it is an absolute priority to get agreement on carbon dioxide emissions, an absolute priority for developed countries to work together to drive renewable energy sources. We won't achieve anything without achieving a peace settlement in the Middle East, but they are stirring up further conflict. So the elite have lost it, but we, the people, have always been the source of revolutionary change.

Think of those people in the cities of Britain in the 1840s being driven off the land by enclosure and working in the squalor of factories, with child labour, illiteracy, cholera and the rest, who then demanded the right to organize at work and form trade unions even though they were illegal. People were sent off to Australia for daring so to do, and yet they marched to demand the vote. When they were not imitating something that had happened elsewhere they had a new vision of their right to be included. Deep historical change always comes from underneath. We have to face how bad it is, how bad the prospects are, and yet not be paralysed by the doom but find the energy to say we can do better than this and, indeed, it will be a better life to lead. And then it has to break out. I think the Transition Towns thing is a bit of a breakout. People are starting to come together and say, 'This isn't party political, but how can we change our town, our village, our place?' I'm hoping Birmingham will move in that direction. And then, of course, the contributions that can be made by political leadership can be thrown up, with new thinking coming from underneath. The engineers and the rest have an enormous contribution to make. Some of the people in this room will have lived through the sixties and whatever you think of that era, it was a time of profound social change. Where did it come from? It was partly due to American students protesting against the Vietnam War and conscription, but it spread across the world, it set up a new set of values. We can do it, but I think we are more atomized than we ever have been before. We have lost the spirit of community and it is harder therefore. But I think more difficult, turbulent times are coming and we will – I'm looking forward to it, actually! – get some spirit back into politics.

Q: You have spoken about how new technologies are advancing and becoming affordable, but we are constantly building new houses every-where without solar panels and without sustainability. Why doesn't the government encourage construction companies to put these in as standard but still make the homes affordable?

Indeed, why don't they? They announced, because it's a sound-bite and it speaks to your concerns, that we are going to have eco-villages or towns or whatever, but one thing we need to do is to improve the insulation of all our housing stock. We need to build better new houses but we also need to improve the whole of our existing housing stock. That's where one of the great savings of energy can be made: just by improving insulation. I understand that Harrogate is a lead-ing example of doing things well. And then if you look at Germany they have a principle that if anyone gets themselves a solar panel or a couple of wind turbines they can connect up to the grid and they get a guaranteed price for [the electricity they produce] – any little business, any home. And there has been a massive growth in con-nections in Germany, much more renewable energy, and all those new technologies, which are the jobs of tomorrow, are flourishing in German industry. So guess what? We think we are clever and we are being stupid. We should do what you say, but we are living with a politics where they are all scared of each other and of Murdoch and they all make announcements to catch the press rather than meaning what they say. It is a disease that is in our political system; they are all in it and we have got to liberate them from it or, if not, replace them.

Q: What I think we have to do is believe in God and his laws.

We have to get fairness and a chance for a decent life. There cannot be a God that wants mayhem, murder and suffering and is still a God of goodness. I am quite a happy person, too, since I left the government particularly, although I did absolutely love my own department and it gave me a real clarity about what a Britain that is trying to create a more just world order could contribute to the world. If we made our development aspirations the centrepiece of our foreign policy we could be a very useful country, we could be very proud of linking up with other countries to create that kind of world order. I think it is very important. This is why I am trying to use this theme of apocalypse – because it always had disaster and hope in it. I think we have got to face how serious it is, but we must not then become so pessimistic that we become absolutely disempowered – because that can happen, if you individualize the pessimistic. That is why we need to come together and say, 'We can do better than this.' I suppose we will never get a world of utter peace and justice, but it wouldn't be hard to do a lot better than this.

Q: I wondered if I could tempt you to a response about Cuba as an example of how people might respond to changing circumstances: the double whammy that they have experienced with the ongoing embargo from the States and the withdrawal of support from the Soviet Union.

As people probably know, the Soviet Union subsidized Cuba, bought its sugar and provided it with oil and so on, and Cuba achieved a miracle in some ways – a massive increase in life expectancy and reduction in infant mortality, and massive improvements in its health-care system. Cuba sent doctors all over the developing world. But it also did some horrible things – it locked up poets and persecuted people of religious conviction. America has behaved in a completely foolish way, but what's new about that? And Europe has always said, 'Stay open with Cuba, trade with Cuba and meet with Cuba and not cut it off, but encourage it to make a democratic transition.' But I understand the point you are referring to, that after the cut-off of Soviet support there was real hunger in Cuba and a big outbreak of illness and blindness. And then they went very big time into allotments and the growth of food organically, throughout the cities and everywhere else, and transformed their consumption of food – a bit like Britain did, as I understand it, during the Second World War, when people kept chickens and pigs in the back garden and grew vegetables everywhere, and the allotment movement and so on. The Totnes Transition Town would argue that we will necessarily have to move towards that way of life as oil gets more and more expensive and fertilizer gets more and more expensive, and it is more difficult to transport things across the world. There will be more of a need for localization in the production of food and, indeed, there could be some joy in that. I assume you are referring to the way in which they produce their food and enjoy producing some wonderful food. The complete romanticization of Cuba worries me a bit, because they do lock up poets and people of religious conviction. I think it is a tragedy that Castro, after the fall of the Soviet Union, did not lead the country to a more open democracy and build on the fantastic things they had achieved. But there is a lot to learn from what they have achieved in growing their own food within the cities that we might well have to do and might enjoy doing. I quite fancy some chickens in my back garden, but the foxes would probably come and get them!

Postscript: The climate change debate continues

JONATHAN DRAPER

A few months after the end of this series of Ebor Lectures on climate change, the world gathered in Copenhagen for the 2009 United Nations Climate Change Conference – COP 15 as it was known. Along with climate pressure groups, high-level delegations and even some national leaders attended. Impassioned speeches were made in urgent and sometimes apocalyptic tones. Given, however, the kind of stark message that stands out from the eminent lectures we listened to in this series, and which form the heart and bulk of this book, we can safely say, no matter how bright the gloss put on it, that the world dropped the ball in Copenhagen. Nothing that would trouble the lives of the great producers of CO_2 was agreed; nothing that would help those most affected by climate change – the poor – was agreed. The 'Accord' that was signed by five of the biggest nations and largest CO_2 producers[1] promised further work and a commitment to continuing to take climate change seriously, and to working towards a binding agreement on the reduction of CO_2 emissions. But we are still a long way off; there remains a great deal to do, and, by all accounts, not a lot of time in which to do it.

Leaked emails and the odd exaggeration about the melting of glaciers in the Himalayas have not helped to settle the minds of the sceptics, in spite of the exceptional clarity of the science, as we saw in these lectures. Indeed, time and again, the science was laid before us and the difficult future it portrays made plain. The responsibility human beings have, at the very least, for trying to do something positive and constructive about it was made equally clear. The message was that we need to act if we are to make the kind of difference that might keep our children and grandchildren from living on an over-heated, under-resourced and degraded earth where the struggle for survival might be grim.

The great climate change debate, however, is not just about the science, however important that might be. As we used to say in our philosophy lectures, an 'is' doesn't necessarily lead to an 'ought'. The fact of a changing climate may lead to different responses and different forms of action. Alongside the science, then, we were told that there is a need for a coherent and committed plan of action. For most of our speakers this centred on various forms of CO_2 reduction, and we heard of many different groups and individuals with ideas of how to reduce carbon production, from the Church of England's 'Shrinking the Footprint'[2] project to the European Union's 20/20 campaign.[3] All spoke of the ways in which local communities and organizations need to be engaged and energized to meet this global challenge.

We also heard expressed with clarity and urgency the message that climate change will affect – is affecting – poor communities in a disproportionately hard way. Climate change is not primarily an intellectual issue or a mere political argument for the people of the Pacific Islands, Bangladesh or the Nile Delta; changing rainfall patterns adversely affect crop production in the poorest parts of sub-Saharan Africa, leading to further poverty and conflict over scarce resources. The Climate Campaign by Christian Aid, for example, targets 'Climate Justice' and the ways in which climate change is already affecting poor people.[4] Climate change is being seen by many as a moral as much as it is a scientific issue, as highlighted by the UN in many reports and conferences over the last decade.

Religious groups will have their part to play too, and few religious leaders have spent as much time and energy on the subject of climate change, or spoken so eloquently about it, as the Archbishop of Canterbury, Dr Rowan Williams. During 2009 alone, the Archbishop gave no fewer than four major lectures on climate change and related issues, including his Ebor Lecture in York Minster in March 2009. In the lecture, Dr Williams spoke for many religious people when he said,

> our care for the world we inhabit is not simply a duty laid upon us but a dimension of life made whole: a redeeming activity grounded in the character of our own redemption, a revelation of the true 'face' of creation as we ourselves undergo the uncovering of our own human face before God.[5]

Not only is our care for creation a moral and spiritual imperative, it is a way in which we live and achieve the fullness of our humanity, one of the ways in which we can know ourselves as complete before God and complete as human beings. Speaking in the House of Lords following COP 15,[6] the Bishop of London, another who has worked tirelessly on climate change issues, and who has shown energetic and effective leadership within the Church of England, pointed not only to the work of the Church of England in respect of climate change, but of how concern about climate change appears right across the religious spectrum, and works to bring the religions closer together:

> The Grand Mufti of Egypt was another participant [in a pre-Copenhagen event]. He outlined a programme of teaching about climate change in Islamic schools. We heard earlier about the extraordinary importance of making profound common cause with the Islamic community, and he has been planning for climate change lessons in Islamic schools, using renewable energy in mosques and the inculcation of green habits in places of pilgrimage. The message is spreading. The Pope, in his New Year message, took as his theme, 'If you want to cultivate peace, protect the creation.'

Among all the religious traditions there is an understanding that climate change is not just about a warming planet and rising seas; it is most profoundly about peace and justice and the nature of our humanity, and therefore of the most profound spiritual importance.

As the significant attendances for this series of lectures attest, many people care passionately about climate change and the significant issues arising from it.[7] In the questions and comments that came at the end of each lecture those who attended expressed real concern that governments, especially those of the world's largest producers of CO_2, won't do enough to prevent catastrophic changes in our climate which will result in profound tragedy not just for human beings but for everything in and on our planet. They were worried but determined, ready to join in the campaigns and solutions of others, from local recycling initiatives to Transition Towns.

Along with what might be called this 'popular concern', there are now also significant numbers of organizations springing up in the UK and around the world which offer advice to companies (including religious organizations) about how to do 'green business' as a response to these issues. 'Green Business Events' are put on where those who offer advice can 'network' with those who need it. The meetings generally offer a pragmatic combination of three elements, and it may be that these are the three elements which will enable the 'carbon corner' to be turned. They are: (1) being green will save you money; (2) being *seen* to be green is essential for the future of your business; and (3) being green is good for the planet. Religious organizations have often focused on the third member of this trinity: it is for the sake of the planet, the sake of the poor and the good of us all that we should act. This, of course, resonates strongly in the hearts and minds of religious people with their faith concerns and priorities. But even religious people feel the pull and the strength of the first of these – that being green can save you money. Religious groups, especially those that inhabit and look after ancient buildings, understand all too well the cost of not being green, and the financial is often just the right kind of incentive to get things moving, to change minds and generate the right kind of activity.

Rowan Williams takes this important economic point a step further. Quoting from an essay by Jonathon Porritt, the Archbishop would like us to discover a new kind of economics. As he suggests:

> An economic world in which environmental responsibility was rewarded, was assumed to be a routine aspect of practice that was both ethically defensible *and* profitable, would have a very different flavour from what we have generally seen for most of the last couple of centuries. And it is also an area in which the pressure of the 'ordinary' consumer can make a perceptible difference.[8]

This is probably the most important matter to arise out of these lectures: that we cannot leave the future of our planet only in the hands of the politicians and the captains of industry. All of us, especially those of us who live affluent lifestyles in high carbon producing countries, have the power and the means to make the changes necessary that can address the great issues that cluster around the theme of climate change. However important the international agreements are (and they are both important and worth working for), they will never turn the tide on their own. As with all the most important issues we face as a world, local solutions need to be found to these global problems. We need to be a part of reimagining our economic and political life to make both more sustainable, to make them fairer and to bring about real solutions to these real problems.

The call that rings through these contributions to the debate about climate change is the need for an intelligent and creative response, and the need to see climate change as an opportunity to think differently about how we live, how we do our economics and politics, how we trade and relate to one another on our one planet. Indeed climate change is not the only pressure pushing fundamental change up the political and moral agenda: the global financial crisis has highlighted just how interconnected these issues are.[9] Perhaps the issue of climate change, coupled with these other pressures, is leading to what the South African theologians under apartheid came to call a *kairos* moment:[10] a crisis that is the stimulus to great change. And because everything is related to everything else, the lifestyle issues raised by climate change need to be supported and encouraged by changes in our political and economic systems. The climate change *kairos* could be a significant opportunity for change.

From a spiritual perspective our response to climate change is a function of how we relate to the world in which we live and of which we are a part. In a Christian context, our world is an environment made specially for us and pronounced very good by our God. As Rowan Williams puts it in his lecture,

> Renewing the face of the earth, then, is an enterprise not of imposing some private human vision on a passive nature but of living in such a way as to bring more clearly to light the interconnectedness of all things and their dependence on what we cannot finally master or understand.[11]

The stewardship we exercise over the earth is a function of our humanity before God. It's that important.

Notes

Introduction

1 For the detailed report, see Frederick R. Wilson (ed.), *The San Antonio Report* (Geneva: WCC, 1990), pp. 52–68. See also 'The Church of England's Seven-Year Plan on Climate Change and Environment' at <http://www.shrinkingthefootprint.cofe.anglican.org/misc_lib/14.pdf>, accessed 15 October 2010.

2 'A sign of hope for the future for people of good will', <http://www.oikoumene.org/gr/resources/documents/wcc-programmes/justice-diakonia-and-responsibility-for-creation/climate-change-water/statement-to-cop15-un-climate-conference-copenhagen.html>, accessed 15 October 2010.

3 'Pontifical Council on Climate Change and Development', <http://www.religiousconsultation.org/News_Tracker/pontifical_council_on_climate_change.htm>, accessed 15 October 2010.

4 *Caritas in Veritate*, <http://www.vatican.va/holy_father/benedict_xvi/encyclicals/documents/hf_ben-xvi_enc_20090629_caritas-in-veritate_en.html>. Accessed 15 October 2010.

5 'The Evangelical Climate Initiative', <http://christiansandclimate.org/>, accessed 15 October 2010.

6 See 'Environment and Climate Change Link', <http://www.ctbi.org.uk/BAA/67/#christian>, accessed 15 October 2010.

7 Celia E. Deane-Drummond, *Eco-theology* (London: Darton, Longman & Todd, 2008), pp. x, xii.

8 Michael Northcott, *A Moral Climate: The Ethics of Global Warming* (London: Darton, Longman & Todd, 2007), pp. 13–16.

9 Michael Northcott, *The Environment and Christian Ethics* (Cambridge: Cambridge University Press, 1996), pp. 164–98.

10 Deane-Drummond, *Eco-theology*, p. 179; pp. 95–6, 181–2. See also Celia E. Deane-Drummond, *The Ethics of Nature* (Oxford: Blackwell, 2004); David Hallman (ed.), *Ecotheology: Voices from South and North* (Geneva: WCC, 1994).

1 Renewing the face of the earth: Human responsibility and the environment

1 Ellen Davis, *Scripture, Culture and Agriculture: An Agrarian Reading of the Bible* (Cambridge: Cambridge University Press, 2008), ch. 5, esp. pp. 90–4.

2 Aelred Squire, *Asking the Fathers* (London: SPCK, 2010), p. 92.
3 Martin Rees, *Our Final Century: Will the Human Race Survive the Twenty-first Century?* (London: Arrow Books, 2003).
4 A. S. Byatt, *The Biographer's Tale* (London: Chatto & Windus, 2000).
5 Paula Clifford, *Angels with Trumpets: The Church in a Time of Global Warming* (London: Darton, Longman & Todd, 2009).
6 Ernst Becker, *The Denial of Death* (London: Collier Macmillan, 1973).
7 Jonathon Porritt, *Capitalism as If the World Matters* (Sterling, VA: Earthscan, 2007), p. 215.
8 Christos Yannaras, *Variations on the Song of Songs* (Holy Cross Orthodox Press, 2005), p. 67.

2 Visions of the end? Revelation and climate change

1 I am following the commentary of Bas Wielenga, *The Book of Revelation* (New Delhi: ISPCK, 2008).
2 James Lovelock, *The Revenge of Gaia: Why the Earth is Fighting Back and How We Can Still Save Humanity* (London: Allen Lane, 2006); Mark Lynas, *Six Degrees: Our Future on a Hotter Planet* (London: Fourth Estate, 2007).
3 Karl Barth, *The Epistle to the Romans* (Oxford: Oxford University Press, 1933), p. 9.
4 Christopher Rowland and Jonathan Roberts, *The Bible for Sinners: Interpretation for the Present Time* (London: SPCK, 2008), p. 58.
5 Jürgen Moltmann, *The Coming of God* (London: SCM, 1996), p. 218.
6 Wielenga, *The Book of Revelation*, p. 63.
7 Wendell Berry, *The Unsettling of America: Culture and Agriculture* (San Francisco: Sierra, 1996), pp. 78, 94.
8 Alastair McIntosh, *Hell and High Water: Climate Change, Hope and the Human Condition* (Edinburgh: Birlinn, 2008), p. 87.
9 McIntosh, *Hell and High Water*, p. 99.
10 Wielenga, *The Book of Revelation*, p. 62.
11 Wielenga, *The Book of Revelation*, p. 64.
12 Walter Wink, *Engaging the Powers: Discernment and Resistance in a World of Domination* (Minneapolis: Fortress, 1992), p. 53, where the passage from Lawrence is also cited.
13 Wielenga, *The Book of Revelation*, p. 66.
14 Wielenga, *The Book of Revelation*, p. 32.
15 Wielenga, *The Book of Revelation*, p. 34.

16 Wielenga, *The Book of Revelation*, p. 81.

17 Moltmann, *The Coming of God*, p. 235.

3 Consider the lilies of the field: Reading Luke's Gospel and saving the planet

1 See <www.wellsforindia.org>.

2 Thomas L. Friedman, 'Mother Nature's Dow', *New York Times* global edition, 31 March 2009.

3 George Monbiot, *Heat: How to Stop the Planet Burning* (Toronto: Doubleday, 2006), cited in Sallie McFague, *A New Climate for Theology* (Minneapolis: Fortress, 2008), p. 25.

4 This was the suggestion of Sallie McFague, *The Body of God* (London: SCM, 1993).

5 Michael Prior, *Jesus, the Liberator: Nazareth Liberation Theology* (Sheffield: Sheffield Academic Press, 1995), pp. 173–5.

6 James Massey, *The Gospel According to Luke*, Dalit Bible commentary, New Testament Vol. 3 (New Delhi: Centre for Dalit Studies, 2007), pp. 69–75.

7 For the relevance of Isaiah's vision today, see Mary Grey, *The Outrageous Pursuit of Hope: Prophetic Dreams for the 21st Century* (London: Darton, Longman & Todd, 2000).

8 Edward Echlin, *Earth Spirituality: Jesus at the Centre* (New Alresford: Arthur James, 1999), pp. 61–70.

9 As related by Joachim Jeremias, *Jerusalem in the Time of Jesus* (London: SCM, 1969), p. 308.

10 The statistics are from the UNEP Report, *Global Environmental Outlook 3 (GEO-3): Past, Present and Future Perspectives* (London: UNEP and Earthscan, 2002), prepared for the Summit on Sustainable Development, Johannesburg 2002.

11 Hwaa Irfan, 'The Environmental Impact on the Palestinian Territories', <www.islamonline.net>. This paragraph paraphrases much of the valuable information of this article, which is mainly a summary of research carried out by Jad Isaac and Belgian researchers at the Applied Research Institute, Jerusalem (ARIJ).

12 Michael Trainor, 'And on Earth Peace, Luke 2.14: Lucan Perspectives on the Earth', in N. Habel (ed.), *Readings from the Perspectives of the Earth*, Earth Bible 1 (Sheffield: Sheffield Academic Press, 2000), pp. 174–92, cited in Celia E. Deane-Drummond, *Eco-theology* (London: Darton, Longman & Todd, 2008), p. 215.

13 Cited in Deane-Drummond, *Eco-theology*, p. 13.

14 Larry Rasmussen, *Earth Community, Earth Ethics* (Maryknoll, NY: Orbis, 1996), pp. 286–7.

15 See James Alison's powerful discussion of society's complicity in these violence cycles: *Faith beyond Resentment* (London: Darton, Longman & Todd, 2001).
16 See Mark Wallace, *Fragments of the Spirit* (New York: Continuum, 1996).
17 Wallace, *Fragments of the Spirit*, p. 170.

4 Hope, hype and honesty reporting global change: A still point on a turning planet

1 Shantanand Saraswati, *Good Company: An Anthology of Sayings, Stories and Answers to Questions.*

5 Disturbing the present

1 Sir Nicholas Stern, Report to the Office of Climate Change (October 2006).

6 The concealments of carbon markets and the publicity of love in a time of climate change

1 Text of the United Nations Framework Convention on Climate Change at <http://unfccc.int/resource/docs/convkp/conveng.pdf>, accessed 17 February 2010.
2 The text of the Copenhagen Accord is part of the minutes of the last day of the Copenhagen conference at <http://unfccc.int/resource/docs/2009/cop15/eng/07.pdf>, accessed 17 February 2010.
3 I. Allison, N. L. Bindoff, R. A. Bindschadler et al., *The Copenhagen Diagnosis: Updating the World on the latest Climate Science* (Sydney: UNSW Climate Change Research Centre, 2009).
4 P. A. Newman, E. R. Nash, A. R. Douglass et al., 'Estimating When the Antarctic Ozone Hole will Recover', in C. Zerefos et al. (eds), *Twenty Years of Ozone Hole Decline* (New York: Springer, 2009), pp. 192–200.
5 L. Lohmann, *Carbon Trading: A Critical Conversation on Climate Change, Privatisation and Power* (Uppsala: Dag Hammarskjöld Centre, 2006), p. 118.
6 See the fuller exposition of Locke's theology of money in M. S. Northcott, *A Moral Climate: The Ethics of Global Warming* (London: Darton, Longman & Todd, 2007).
7 J. Locke, *Second Treatise of Civil Government*, Section 46.
8 B. N. Nelson, *The Idea of Usury: From Tribal Brotherhood to Universal Otherhood* (Chicago: University of Chicago Press, 1969), pp. 73–82.
9 M. Luther, *On the Jews and Their Lies* in *Luther's Works*, Volume 47, ed. Franklin Sherman (Augsburg, MN: Fortress Press, 1971), p. 211. See also B. Stephenson and S. Power Bratton, 'Martin Luther's Understanding of Sin's Impact on Nature and the Unlanding of the Jew', *Ecotheology*, 9 (2000), pp. 84–102.

10 J. Milbank, 'Pleonasm, Speech and Writing', in J. Milbank, *The Word Made Strange: Theology, Language, and Culture* (Oxford: Blackwell, 1997), p. 58.

11 A. McIntosh, 'What Price the Earth?', *World Mission* 33 (February 2010), <www.alastairmcintosh.com/articles/2010-CofS-WM-Climate.pdf>, accessed 21 February 2010.

12 A. Leopold, *A Sand County Almanac and Sketches Here and There* (Oxford: Oxford University Press, 1968).

13 M. Northcott, *The Environment and Christian Ethics* (Cambridge: Cambridge University Press, 1996).

14 C. Wilson, 'From Limits to Laws: The Construction of the Nomological Image of Nature in Early Modern Philosophy', in L. Daston and M. Stolleis (eds), *Natural Law and Laws of Nature in Early Modern Europe* (Farnham: Ashgate, 2008), pp. 13–28.

15 C. Taylor, *The Sources of the Self* (Cambridge: Cambridge University Press, 2009).

16 A. Naess, 'The Shallow and the Deep, Long-range Ecology Movements: A Summary', *Inquiry* 16 (1973), pp. 95–100; H. Rolston III, *Environmental Ethics: Duties to and Values in the Natural World* (Philadelphia: Temple University Press, 1988).

17 M. Callon and B. Latour, 'Unscrewing the Big Leviathan: how actors macro-structure reality and how sociologists help them to do so', in K. Knorr-Cetina and A. V. Cicourel (eds), *Advances in Social Theory and Methodology: Toward an Integration of Micro- and Macro-Sociologies* (London: Routledge and Kegan Paul, 1981), pp. 277–303.

18 S. Hauerwas, 'A Worldly Church: Politics, Theology and the Common Good', in P. M. Candler and C. Cunningham (eds), *The Grandeur of Reason: Religion, Tradition and Universalism* (London: SCM Press, 2010), pp. 9–28.

19 A. MacIntyre, 'Politics, Philosophy and the Common Good', in Kelvin Knight (ed.), *The MacIntyre Reader* (Notre Dame, IN: Notre Dame University Press, 1998), pp. 234–52.

20 L. Lebel, A. Contreras, S. Pasong et al., 'Nobody Knows Best: Alternative Perspectives on Forest Management in Southeast Asia', *International Environmental Agreements: Politics, Law and Economics* 4 (June 2004), pp. 111–27.

21 E. Ostrom, *Governing the Commons: The Evolution of Institutions for Collective Action* (Cambridge: Cambridge University Press, 1990).

22 J. T. Roberts and B. C. Parks, *Climate of Injustice* (Cambridge, MA: MIT Press), pp. 188–9.

23 P. Merowski, *More Heat than Light: Economics as Social Physics, Physics as Nature's Economics* (Cambridge: Cambridge University Press, 1989).

24 W. B. Wriston, *The Twilight of Sovereignty: How the Information Revolution is Transforming Our World* (New York: Charles Scribner and Sons, 1992).

25 K. Barth, 'Near and Distant Neighbours', in K. Barth, *Church Dogmatics III.4: The Doctrine of Creation*, trans. A. T. Mackay, T. H. L. Parker et al. (Edinburgh: T & T Clark, 1961), pp. 285–323.

26 On the Christian origins of fair trade see M. S. Northcott, 'Fair Trade and Human Wellbeing' in I. Steedman, J. Atherton and E. Graham (eds), *The Practices of Happiness: Political Economy, Religion and Wellbeing* (London: Routledge, 2010).

27 G. Moore, 'The Fair Trade Movement: Parameters, Issues and Future Research', *Journal of Business Ethics* 53 (August 2004), pp. 73–86.

28 For a fuller account see M. S. Northcott, 'The World Trade Organization, Fair Trade and the Body Politics of Saint Paul', in John Atherton (ed.), *Through the Eye of a Needle: Theology, Ethics and Economy* (London: Epworth Press, 2007), pp. 169–88.

29 Rowan Williams, '"Act for the sake of love": Archbishop of Canterbury preaches in Copenhagen Cathedral', <http://www.archbishopofcanterbury.org/2673>, accessed 16 February 2010.

30 Williams, 'Act for the sake of love'.

31 C. Yannaras, *The Freedom of Morality* (Crestwood, NY: St Vladimir Seminary Press, 1984), pp. 76–9.

32 *The Fifty Spiritual Homilies of Makarios* 5.5, cited in Yannaras, *The Freedom of Morality*, p. 78.

33 Isaac the Syrian, *Mystic Treatises* 81, cited in Yannaras, *Freedom of Morality*, p. 80.

34 C. Smidt, 'Introduction', in Corwin Smidt (ed.), *Religion as Social Capital: Producing the Common Good* (Waco, TX: Baylor University Press, 2003), p. 9.

35 S. Kierkegaard, *Works of Love*, trans. H. and E. Hong (New York: Harper, 1962), pp. 11–17.

7 Exploring a public theology for here on earth

1 Tim Flannery, *Here on Earth: An Argument for Hope* (Melbourne: Text Publishing, 2010).

2 Charles Mathewes, *A Theology of Public Life* (Cambridge: Cambridge University Press, 2007), pp. 1–2.

3 Seán McDonagh, *Climate Change: The Challenge to All of Us* (Dublin: The Columba Press), 2006.

4 Edward P. Echlin, *Climate and Christ: A Prophetic Alternative* (Dublin: The Columba Press), 2010.

5 John W. de Gruchy, 'Public Theology as Christian Witness: Exploring the Genre', *International Journal of Public Theology* 1:1 (2007), pp. 26–42.

6 Sallie McFague, *The Body of God: An Ecological Theology* (Minneapolis: Augsburg Fortress, 1993); *Life Abundant: Rethinking Theology for a Planet in Peril* (Minneapolis: Augsburg Fortress, 2001); *A New Climate for Theology: God, the World and Global Warming* (Minneapolis: Augsburg Fortress, 2008).

7 Celia E. Deane-Drummond, *Eco-theology* (London: Darton, Longman & Todd, 2008).

8 Ernst Conradie, *An Ecological Christian Anthropology: At Home on Earth?* (Aldershot and Burlington: Ashgate, 2005).

9 Denis Edwards, *Jesus the Wisdom of God: An Ecological Theology* (Maryknoll, NY: Orbis, 1995).

10 Barbara Rossing, 'Hastening the Day when the Earth Will Burn: Global Warming, 2 Peter and the Book of Revelation', in Cynthia Briggs Kitteridge, Ellen Bradshaw Aitken and Jonathan A. Draper (eds), *The Bible in the Public Square* (Minneapolis: Fortress, 2008), pp. 25–38.

11 Michael Northcott, *A Moral Climate: The Ethics of Global Warming* (London: Darton, Longman & Todd, 2007).

12 Daniel Munteanu, 'Cosmic Liturgy: The Theological Dignity of Creation as a Basis of an Orthodox Ecotheology', *International Journal of Public Theology* 4:3 (2010), pp. 332–44.

13 John Zizioulas, 'Preserving God's Creation: Three Lectures on Theology and Ecology', *King's Theological Review* (Spring 1989), pp. 1–5; (Autumn 1989), pp. 41–5; (Spring 1990), pp. 1–5.

14 McFague, *A New Climate for Theology*, p. 31.

15 Sallie McFague, 'The World as God's Body', *The Christian Century* (20–27 July 1988), pp. 671–3.

16 See chapter 6 of the present volume by Michael Northcott, 'The concealments of carbon markets and the publicity of love in a time of climate change'.

17 John Houghton, 'Foreword', in Michael Northcott, *A Moral Climate: The Ethics of Global Warming* (London, Darton, Longman & Todd, 2007), p. 1.

18 Phillip Sipiora, 'Introduction: The Ancient Concept of *Kairos*', in Phillip Sipiora and James S. Baumlin (eds), *Rhetoric and Kairos: Essays in History, Theory and Praxis* (Albany: State University of New York Press, 2002), pp. 1–9.

19 Ernst Conradie, 'Climate Change – the Coming Decade of Truth for God's Household', NECSSA climate change document (2009), <http://www.safcei.org.za/news/view.php?id=72>, accessed 1 April 2010. The notion of climate change presenting the world with a *kairos* moment is especially evident in the work of the Canadian initiative for ecumenical justice. See <http://www.kairoscanada.org/en/ecojustice/>.

20 John Vidal, 'Vulnerable Nations at Copenhagen Summit Reject 2C Target', *The Guardian*, 10 December 2009.

21 John Vidal, 'Copenhagen Deal Breaks Down as Developing Nations Split Over 'Tuvalu Protocol', *The Guardian*, 9 December 2009.

22 Northcott, *A Moral Climate*, p. 3.

23 Robert Schreiter, *The New Catholicity: Theology Between the Local and the Global* (Maryknoll, NY: Orbis, 1997), p. 19.

24 Jione Havea, 'The Politics of Climate Change: A Talanoa from Oceania', *International Journal of Public Theology* 4:3 (2010), pp. 345–55.

25 Mark Hayes, 'We Are All Tuvaluans', *Griffith Review* 12 (2006).

26 Maina Talia, 'Towards *Fatele* Theology: A Contextual Theological Response in Addressing Threats of Global Warming in Tuvalu', M.Th. thesis, unpublished, 2009, Tainan Theological College and Seminary; Tafue Lusama, 'Punishment of the Innocent: The Problem of Global Warming with Special Reference to Tuvalu', M.Th. thesis, unpublished, 2004, Tainan Theological College and Seminary.

27 H. Paul Santmire, *The Travail of Nature: The Ambiguous Ecological Promise of Christian Theology* (Minneapolis: Fortress, 1985).

28 See Earth Bible Project Team, 'Guiding Ecojustice Principles', in Norman Habel (ed.), *Readings from the Perspective of the Earth* (Sheffield: Sheffield Academic Press, 2000), pp. 38–53.

29 Ernst Conradie, 'Climate Change and the Common Good: Some Reflections from the South African Context', *International Journal of Public Theology* 4:3 (2010), pp. 271–93.

30 Clive Hamilton, *Requiem for a Species: Why We Resist the Truth about Climate Change* (Sydney: Allen and Unwin, 2010).

31 Michael Novacek, *Terra: Our 100-Million-Year-Old Ecosystem – and the Threats that Now Put it at Risk* (New York: Farrar, Strauss & Giroux, 2007).

32 Leonardo Boff, *Global Civilization: Challenges to Society and Christianity* (London and Louisville, KY: Equinox, 2003), pp. 75–82.

33 Christopher Booker, *The Real Global Warming Disaster: Is the Obsession with 'Climate Change' Turning Out To Be the Most Costly Scientific Blunder in History?* (London and New York: Continuum, 2009).

34 Christopher Booker and Richard North, *Scared to Death: from BSE to Global Warming. Why Scares Are Costing us the Earth* (London and New York: Continuum, 2007).

35 Scott Bader-Saye, *Following Jesus in a Culture of Fear* (Grand Rapids, MI: Brazos, 2007).

36 Alastair Hannay, *On the Public: Thinking in Action* (Abingdon/New York: Routledge, 2005).

37 Jennifer Marohasy, 'John Howard, Environmentalist', *Institute of Public Affairs Review* (December 2007), pp. 33–5.

38 Clive Hamilton, *Scorcher: The Dirty Politics of Climate Change* (Melbourne: Black Inc Agenda, 2007).

39 *The Garnaut Climate Change Review*, <http://www.garnautreview.org.au>.

40 Kevin Rudd, 'Address to the UN Bali Conference on Climate Change', <http://australianpolitics.com/2007/12/12/rudd-address-to-bali-climate-change-conference.shtml>, accessed 1 April 2010.

41 Peter Manley Scott, 'The Future as God's Amnesty? A Public Theology of Resistance for a Changing Climate', *International Journal of Public Theology* 4:3 (2010), pp. 314–31.

42 Flannery, *Here on Earth*, p. 280.

8 Apocalypse now: Global equity and sustainable living – the preconditions for human survival

1 Lester R. Brown, 'Learning From China', *USA Today*, Society for the Advancement of Education (July 2005), <http://findarticles.com/p/articles/mi_m1272/is_2722_134/ai_n14814239/?tag=content;col1>.

2 United Nations, 'Millennium Ecosystem Assessment' (Washington DC: Island Press, 2001).

Postscript: The climate change debate continues

1 The USA, China, India, Brazil and South Africa. Reports on COP15 can be found at the UN Climate Change web site: <http://unfccc.int>.

2 See <http://www.shrinkingthefootprint.cofe.anglican.org/>.

3 See <http://ec.europa.eu/environment/climat/climate_action.htm>.

4 Information about Christian Aid's campaign can be found at <www.christianaid.org.uk>.

5 See p. 12 of the present volume.

6 The Rt Revd and Rt Hon. Richard Chartres, Bishop of London, spoke in the Lords (14 January 2010) in the debate on the Copenhagen conference on climate change initiated by Lord Stone of Blackheath.

7 A thousand people turned out to hear the Archbishop of Canterbury give his lecture: an average of 350 attended each of the others – more

than 3,000 people attending from in and around the small city of York.

8 See p. 9 of the present volume.

9 The 2009–10 Ebor Lectures explore the issues that arise from the global financial crisis.

10 The text of the 1985 Kairos Document can be found at <www.sahistory. org.za/pages/library-resources/officialdocs/kairos-document.htm>.

11 See p. 10 of the present volume.

Index

Page ranges in **bold** denote whole chapters.

J. B. 'Billy' Mathews

J.B. 'Billy' Mathews, 1847-1904
by Bruce & Todd, Roswell, NM, c. 1896
Courtesy: Jesse and Lillian Bates, Elk, New Mexico

J. B. 'Billy' Mathews

Biography of a

Lincoln County Deputy

Elvis E. Fleming

Yucca Tree Press

First Printing   April 1999

Fleming, Elvis E.

    J.B. 'BILLY' MATHEWS: Biography of a Lincoln County Deputy
        1. Mathews, J.B.   2. Lincoln County War.   3. New Mexico
        Territorial History - Lincoln County War.
        I. Elvis E. Fleming.   II. Title.

Library of Congress Catalog Card Number: 98-061627

ISBN: 1-881325-29-6

Cover design: Fine Line Design

Table of Contents

List of Illustrations

List of Maps

Acknowledgments

Many people helped me reconstruct the life of Billy Mathews, and I am greatly indebted to them for their assistance. I received much help from relatives of Mathews and his wife, Dora Bates Mathews. Jesse and Lillian Bates of Elk, New Mexico, allowed the use of their photograph collection and provided general information about the Bates family and the Peñasco Valley. Jesse is the grandson of Ralph Bates, Dora Mathews' brother. I interviewed Billy and Dora Mathews' granddaughter, the late Bess Maddux Dow, in Roswell in 1983. In recent years I have had several interviews with the Mathews' great-granddaughter, Joanne Williamson McCombs of Roswell, and also with her daughter, Betty Patton; I was a former colleague of Betty's at Eastern New mexico University-Roswell. Other relatives interviewed were Richard R. 'Dick' Armstrong and his wife Joanne of Santa Fe, and Jan Armstrong Neuenschwander of Houston. Dick and Jan are great-grandchildren of Billy and Dora Mathews. I greatly appreciate all of these contributions.

James A. Dillon, Jr., of McMinnville, Tennessee, the official historian of Warren County, helped me considerably with sources on the Civil War. Lillian Bidal of Albuquerque was very generous in sharing her great knowledge of the Peñasco Valley and the CA Bar Ranch, not only in her books but in letters and telephone interviews as well. Several present and former residents of the Peñasco Valley helped me to gain a better understanding of the area, including Ernestine Chesser Williams, Melvin and Mary Helen Cleve Foley, and the late T. Edsil Runyan.

The staffs of several institutions have been instrumental in facilitating my research. These include the Historical Center for Southeast New Mexico, Roswell; the Rio Grande Historical Collections, New Mexico State University, Las Cruces; the Learning Resource Center at Eastern New Mexico University-Roswell; and the Chaves County Clerk's office in Roswell.

I am most grateful to Dr. David Townsend of Alamogordo, New Mexico for his critique on my Lincoln County War chapter. My bride of forty-three years, Menza Fleming, with her expertise in English and history, has rendered invaluable aid as proof-reader, critic, and encourager.

It is my desire that readers will find this account to be a worthy addition to the historical literature of New Mexico. If there are errors of fact or interpretation, I accept the responsibility. Perhaps this volume will elicit additional documents pertaining to Jacob Basil 'Billy' Mathews.

Elvis E. Fleming
Roswell, NM
April 1999

Foreword

So much has been written about the Lincoln County War, and more particularly about Billy the Kid, that the feeling grows that enough is enough. Nothing could be farther from the truth. So much of what has been written has been bad—again, particularly about the Kid—that a good book is welcome to the field. Elvis Fleming's study of J.B. (Billy) Mathews is a good addition indeed. Please do not misunderstand. There have been some fine studies of the war and recently some good reassessments of the career of Billy the Kid. However, two things have been generally missing from a complete view of the war.

One missing ingredient has been the attempt to place the war in a larger context of time and place. John Wilson's study *Merchants, Guns, and Money* is effective in placing the war in the larger context of the whole history of Lincoln County, and more recently John Ryan's *Fort Stanton and Its Community, 1855-1896* deals well with the "symbiotic relationship" between that military installation and the surrounding area. This relationship helps understand how the war fit into the larger economic context. More works like these are needed.

Still another missing element in understanding the Lincoln County War has been the lack of definition given to some of the major players and minor characters in the war. This is to say that Billy the Kid has so overshadowed the other participants that they seem to have existence only as background figures to this archetypical western hero-badman. Without getting involved in the exigencies of this situation, or the fairness of it, suffice it to say that many of these lesser figures need to be given a fuller definition. Many of them are much more interesting than the Kid and lived lives of much more value. Such a one is J.B. (Billy) Mathews.

Elvis Fleming's study speaks to both of these missing factors. It gives the reader a larger context to understand those who were drawn into the war. In fact, the war is covered in only one of Fleming's six chapters. Mathews' life is analyzed both before and after that traumatic event, and the war is thus placed in a proper framework. Fleming, using the approach he does, prevents Billy the Kid from crowding Billy Mathews off the stage. Mathews emerges as full-rounded, not always admirable, but generally as a good man drawn into exciting events. He is also more fun to read about than Billy the Kid.

I am glad Elvis Fleming undertook this study. I think it can become a model of what needs to be done relative to the Lincoln County War. No one is more qualified. He is the preeminent historian on the southeastern part of New Mexico, and this area has to be understood to really understand Billy Mathews. I am also pleased Yucca Tree Press teamed with Elvis in this work. This press is emerging as one of the premier publishers of historical material in the state.

If more works of this quality appear, we may come to understand the Lincoln County War a bit better. We may never understand why someone like Billy the Kid is considered to be more interesting than 'Buckshot' Roberts or Dick Brewer or Billy Mathews or a host of others.

David Townsend
Alamogordo, New Mexico

Introduction

Jacob B. 'Billy' Mathews performed a leading role in what is arguably the most notorious chapter in the history of the American West: New Mexico's Lincoln County War of the 1870s. While he was carrying out orders from one or another of the primary figures in the conflict, namely J.J. 'Jimmy' Dolan or Sheriff William Brady, Mathews took part in practically all of the significant events of the war.

After his experiences in the Lincoln conflict, he became a distinguished pioneer in the establishment of big-time cattle ranching in the Peñasco Valley and farming in the Pecos Valley of Southeast New Mexico. He was the postmaster of Roswell, New Mexico, from 1898 until his death in 1904.

In the Lincoln County War, Mathews was an important leader whose adventures made up a considerable part of the action. However, he has usually been outshone by the first-echelon characters such as William H. 'Billy the Kid' Bonney, Lawrence G. Murphy, Dolan, Brady, Alexander McSween, John Henry Tunstall, Pat Garrett, and John Chisum.

Mathews' primary claim to fame is that he was the sheriff's chief deputy in command of the posse that shot down John Henry Tunstall on February 18, 1878, thereby igniting the most celebrated event in Lincoln County's history.

What is known about Mathews' life before the Lincoln County War is quite meager, and much of what has been published about him

Billy Mathews

is incorrect. This account will seek to rectify the inaccuracies as well as to provide new information on his life both before and after the Lincoln County War.

Unlike many of his colleagues in Lincoln, Mathews was not a native of Ireland, as Joel Jacobsen implies in his 1994 book, *Such Men as Billy the Kid: The Lincoln County War Reconsidered*. While Mathews was proud of his Scotch-Irish ancestry, he actually was born in Tennessee. His parents, Walter Mathews and Antalise 'Anna' Ashford, were married in Woodbury, Cannon County, on April 20, 1842, when Walter was about twenty-one years old and Anna was about fifteen. According to Mathews' descendants in Roswell, family tradition has it that Walter was known as 'George' and Anna was known as 'Sally.' How this discrepancy in names came about is unknown. Walter's paternal grandparents came from Ireland, and his mother's people came from England. Walter Mathews' farm was located on Stones River about five miles from Woodbury, and that farm was the place where their children were born.

The Census of 1850 lists the children of Walter and Anna Mathews as Josiah, 7; John, 5; J.B., 3; and Nancy, 1. The subject of this account, Jacob Basil (J.B.) Mathews, was born on May 5, 1847. An 1895 book, *An Illustrated History of New Mexico*, presents the first brief biography of Mathews. It states that J.B. acquired his education "in the district schools of the neighborhood, his privileges being somewhat meager, for just as he was about to enter school in Nashville, the Civil War broke out and his plans were in consequence changed."

Family tradition also has it that two additional sons and three additional daughters were born after Nancy's birth in 1849. J.B.'s two younger brothers were Jim Louis and Robert Lee ('Bob'). These two lived for a time in Texas and were known to the New Mexico branch of the family, although Jim Louis never visited the Territory. J.B.'s descendants never knew the older brothers and the names of the other sisters are unknown. Strangely, the Walter Mathews family does not appear in the 1860 or 1870 censuses for Tennessee, although *An Illustrated History* states that J.B.'s parents spent their entire lives in Tennessee.

I

J. B. MATHEWS' OTHER WAR

Since Tennessee was a border state during the Civil War, it was to be expected that people's loyalties would be divided between the North and the South. Union loyalists were clustered in the eastern portion of the state, and Confederate forces held that area for most of the war. The war spread across the middle and western parts of the state in 1862, and the Federals established control of those areas. The Mathews family lived in Middle Tennessee, where most people supported the Rebel cause.

The mistaken notion that J.B. Mathews served in the Confederate Cavalry has appeared in print several times. *An Illustrated History of New Mexico* simply names his military unit without specifying whether it was a Rebel or a Yankee regiment. The account also states that he entered the army "at the very commencement of the struggle ...," when he would have been barely fourteen years of age. That would have been possible, of course, but the claim does not coincide with his known military record. Further, the article asserts that Mathews fought in the battle of Murfreesboro or Stones River. Actually, that battle was fought months before Mathews' enlistment. Why this incorrect information is included in the account in *An Illustrated History* is not clear. Since it was written during Mathews' lifetime, one would assume that the writer secured the information directly from him or would have at least provided him an opportunity to correct any errors or misconceptions. The *Roswell Register*, a weekly newspaper, reported on May 13, 1898, that Mathews had enlisted in the "federal army"; but other information in that article is known to be incorrect.

Upon Mathews' death in 1904, the *Roswell Daily Record* and the weekly *Roswell Record* both repeated most of the biography from *An Illustrated History.* The news item about his death in the *Roswell Register* does state that he was in the Union army.

The idea that Mathews was in the Confederate army apparently started with a story in a special historical edition of the *Roswell Daily Record* on October 7, 1937. The article quotes *An Illustrated History* "verbatim" but adds a flag heading: "In Confederate Army." The editor may have assumed, as many others did, that if Mathews lived in Tennessee, he must have been a Confederate.

Several articles and books about the Lincoln County War published since 1937 have perpetuated this fallacious belief. Maurice Garland Fulton, for example, in *History of the Lincoln County War* (1968) states, "Mathews was a Tennessean and an ex-Confederate soldier." Likewise, Frederick Nolan, in his more recent *The Lincoln County War: A Documentary History* (1992), writes, "... Mathews was one of the few proponents of the troubles who had fought on the Confederate side during the Civil War; .... ."

Although James D. Shinkle, prolific historian of Roswell in the 1950's and 1960's, repeats in *Reminiscences of Roswell Pioneers* (1966) the notion that Mathews was in the Confederate army, he actually believed that Mathews served in the Northern army. He never pursued the matter, according to Mathews' granddaughter, Bess Dow, of Roswell; but Shinkle was aware that Mathews' widow drew a pension as the widow of a Union soldier. Documentary proof of Mathews' Union service from the National Archives has been lacking in earlier books and articles, and was first presented in print by the present writer in an article in the *New Mexico Historical Review*, July 1997.

J. B. Mathews actually served in the 5th Tennessee Cavalry Regiment, which was a Union outfit—not Confederate. This regiment was also called the '1st Middle Tennessee Cavalry Regiment,' and sometimes erroneously called the '1st Tennessee Cavalry Regiment: 5th

East Tennessee Cavalry Regiment.' This information, as well as much of the following information about the 5th Tennessee, is taken from *Tennesseans in the Civil War*, a two-volume work published in 1965 by the Tennessee Civil War Centennial Commission.

Governor Andrew Johnson authorized former Congressman William B. Stokes to raise a cavalry battalion in June 1862, and the first companies mustered in at Nashville in September. The field officers consisted of Stokes as colonel, with two lieutenant-colonels and five majors under him.

The chief responsibility of 'Stokes' Regiment' was guarding Union supply lines between Nashville and various fronts to the south and southeast toward Chattanooga. The main battle in which the 5th Tennessee Cavalry took part before J. B. Mathews enlisted was Stones River, or Murfreesboro, December 26, 1862, to January 5, 1863. The outfit fought numerous skirmishes and battles after that, the most important being at Franklin on April 10, 1863. The Union staged a major offensive in the fall of 1863 when federal troops took Chattanooga, but the 5th Tennessee had no direct role in that action.

According to Bess Dow, family tradition is that J.B.'s father and one brother enlisted in the Confederate army. Confederate records in the National Archives in Washington show that one Walter 'Mathis,' also shown as 'Mathews,' enlisted in Colonel Mathias Martin's 23rd Tennessee Infantry Regiment on August 23 or 24, 1861, at Camp Trousdale, Tennessee, for ten months. The enlisting officer was Lieutenant G.H. Smith. It is not clear how the surname could be spelled as both 'Mathis' and 'Mathews'—possibly a spelling error by the enlisting officer. Walter Mathews was in Captain M.M. Brien, Jr.'s Company 'H,' which indeed included men from Mathews' home county of Cannon. Records show that this regiment moved to Bowling Green, Kentucky, in October 1861, where Mathews was discharged on January 9, 1862, by John Pope. He apparently saw little or no action. Whether or not this man was J. B. Mathews' father cannot be determined for certain, but no clearer records exist and it does seem reasonable to assume that this is a correct identification.

Efforts to establish whether J.B.'s older brothers, John or Josiah Mathews, served in a Confederate outfit have not been successful.

Tennessee Confederate records show eight men named 'John Mathews,' four named 'John Matthews,' and four named 'John Mathis.' In addition, another forty-one men with these surnames have one or more 'J' initials. One John Mathis served in the 23rd Infantry. None of these can be authenticated as a son of Walter Mathews. The only 'Josiah' with any of these surnames was a surgeon in the 46th Infantry.

Family legend says that sixteen-year-old J. B. ran away from home and tried unsuccessfully to enlist in the Confederate army. For unknown reasons, he then joined the Union forces—as the legend goes—and fought against his father and/or brother. However, his father's military service likely ended before J.B. enlisted.

On October 19, 1863, sixteen-year-old Jacob enlisted at McMinnville, which is in Warren County just east of Cannon County, in Stokes' cavalry regiment for three years of service. In an apparent attempt to conceal his identity (or possibly through a spelling error by the enlisting officer), he enlisted under the name of 'Jacob B. Mathis.' He secured the services of one John D. Rigsby to help him enlist. The illiterate Rigsby claimed he was the youth's "lawful guardian" and placed his mark on the papers to give his consent for Mathews to enlist, both asserting that he was eighteen years of age. Captain James Clift, a Warren County farmer and merchant, was the recruiting officer; the witness who signed the papers was Norman Winnett. John Bennett, surgeon of the 19th Regiment, Michigan Infantry Volunteers, gave 'Mathis' his physical examination. The enlistment record describes J.B. Mathis as five feet, five inches tall; fair complexion; blue eyes; and fair hair. It lists his occupation as "farmer."

All the records indicate that Mathews was in Company 'M' from the beginning of his service, but the records also state that the company was not organized until after February 24, 1864. The Third Brigade, Second Division of the U.S. Cavalry Corps, of which the 5th Tennessee Cavalry was a part, was broken up on November 8, 1864. The 'First Middle Tennessee Cavalry' was then assigned to the First Brigade, Second Division. However, the division was reorganized two days later, and Major-General George H. Thomas gave orders for the 5th Tennessee to "... proceed to Nashville, without delay, to

| M. | 5 Cav. | Tenn. |

Jacob M. Mathis

Co. , 5 Reg't Tennessee Cavalry.

18 , years.

ears on a

Detachment Muster-in Roll

the organization named above. Roll dated

Nashville, Tenn., May 31, 186 4

ster-in to date Oct. 19, 186 3

ed for duty and enrolled:

en Oct. 19 , 186 3

re McMinnville, Tenn.

iod 3 years.

ation of horse, $ 100

ation of horse equipments, $ 100

arks:

erreta by Soffane E

k mark:

McQuinn Ten

| M. | 5 Cav. | Tenn. |

Jacob M. Mathis

Co. , 5 Reg't Tennessee Cavalry.

Appears on

Company Muster Roll

for May & June , 1864

Present or absent Present

Stoppage, $ 100 for

Due Gov't, $ 100 for

Valuation of horse, $ 100

Valuation of horse equipments, $ 100

Remarks: On fur from

late by enlistment

Book mark:

S. Lawton

| M. | 5 Cav. | Tenn. |

Sergt J.B. Mathis

Sgt , Co. M, 5 Reg't Tennessee Cavalry.

Appears on

Company Muster Roll

for July & Aug , 186 4

Present or absent Present

Stoppage, $ 100 for

Due Gov't, $ 100 for

Valuation of horse, $ 100

Valuation of horse equipments, $ 100

Remarks: Killed, returned

been since sept 18 64

Book mark:

F. Evans

J.B. Mathews' military records: 'Detachment Muster-in Roll,' May 31, 1864; 'Company Muster Roll,' May/June 1864; 'Company Muster Roll,' July/August 1864; 5th Tennessee Cavalry Regiment, Co. 'M.' (Name shown as 'Mathis.') *National Archives, Washington, DC.*

J.B. Mathews' military records: 'Returns,' November 1864; 'Company Muster Roll,' November/December 1864; 'Company Muster Roll,' September/October 1864; 5th Tennessee Cavalry Regiment, Co. 'M.' (Name shown as 'Mathis.') *National Archives, Washington, DC.*

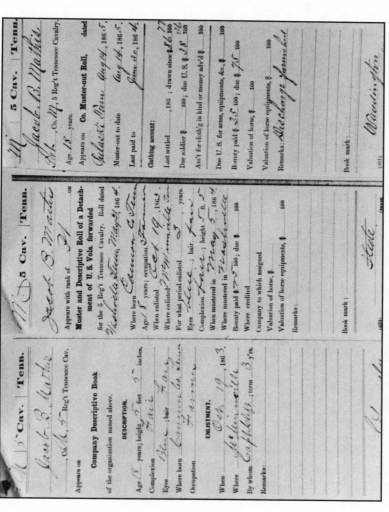

J.B. Mathews' military records: 'Company Descriptive Book,' October 19, 1863; 'Muster and Descriptive Roll of A Detachment of U.S. Vols. forwarded,' May 31, 1864; 'Co. Muster-out Roll,' August 14, 1865. 5th Tennessee Cavalry Regiment, Co. 'M.' (Name shown as 'Mathis.') *National Archives, Washington, DC.*

reorganize and complete its muster." The outfit was in Nashville until January 24, 1864, when Stokes received orders to move out to Sparta to destroy the Confederate guerrillas who infested that area. In the meantime, on January 10, 1864, General Thomas recommended that the regiment be divided into two regiments under the commands of Stokes and Lieutenant-Colonel Robert Galbraith.

Contemporary documents reveal that some officers of the regular U.S. Army were contemptuous toward the 5th Tennessee Cavalry. On January 30, 1864, for example, according to *Tenneseeans in the Civil War:*

> ... Major General Lovell H. Rousseau, at Nashville, reported the troops in the District were generally under good discipline, well equipped, and in good condition, 'excepting, of course, the 5th Tennessee Cavalry under Colonel Stokes, and a few others, who are neither well drilled, disciplined, or equipped... .'

Rousseau supported the idea of separating Stokes' and Galbraith's battalions. However, Stokes was opposed to the idea and apparently had more pull with Governor Johnson than General Rousseau had. The regiment was never divided.

James A. Dillon, Jr., of McMinnville, long-time resident and official historian of Warren County, Tennessee, writes that the 5th Tennessee Cavalry:

> ... was composed of misfits who held little affection or loyalty to either side. In most cases the enlistees were coerced into joining the unit for a variety of reasons: money from enlistment bonuses, contraband obtained by preying on Confederate sympathizers, and food. In many cases, the enlistees came from families left completely destitute by the conflict. Many of the stories handed down by the families as well as letters and diaries left by survivors verify the above statements ... .

Other contemporary historians set forth a more tempered view of the 5th Tennessee, holding that the regiment was less mercenary than depicted by Dillon. Some assert that the guerrillas against which the

5th Tennessee was fighting were not so much Confederate loyalists as profiteers or opportunists.

Perhaps the motivations suggested by Dillon applied to young J.B. Mathews, who was promised a bounty for enlisting. The company muster roll for December 31, 1863, through April 30, 1864, states that Mathews was present and was due a $25.00 bounty and a $2.00 premium. Another document indicates that he received the bounty on May 5, 1864 (which happened to be Mathews' seventeenth birthday), and that 'Mathis' mustered in at Nashville with the rank of Private. This probably was the time when Company 'M' organized, but incomplete records make it impossible to determine what Mathews had been doing since his enlistment the previous October. The muster roll for May and June states that all of Mathews' pay was due from the date of enlistment.

As commanded, Colonel Stokes moved to Sparta around the first of February 1864. His reports indicate that he started with 150 men, but other companies joined him and brought the total strength up to 200. On February 18, Stokes' regiment, consisting of Companies 'A,' 'B,' 'G,' 'I,' 'K,' and 'L,' fought Confederate troops under Hughs, Hamilton, Ferguson, Carter, and Bledsoe. Another battle with the same participants took place on February 22 on Calfkiller Creek. Two days later, parts of Companies 'C,' 'F,' and 'H' joined Stokes, thus bringing representatives of all companies together in one place for the first time in many months. Exceptions to this were two Alabama companies under Colonel Streight which had been captured by the Rebels, and Company 'M,' which was organized later and which included Mathews. Most of the men of Companies 'C,' 'F,' and 'H' were at Nashville and were dismounted because they had no horses.

Stokes reported many skirmishes in February and March 1864 in the vicinity of Sparta, Calfkiller, and Beersheba. He combed the countryside for guerrillas in the counties of Jackson, Putnam, and Overton. He emphasized to the commander how important it was to remount his troops; he also asked to have them armed with Springfield rifles.

Brigadier General William S. Smith, Chief of Cavalry, was not impressed. His response to Stokes was:

You have no idea of the demands made upon our Government for horses to remount our cavalry. No one Government—not all the Governments of the world—could keep so much cavalry mounted while animals are so recklessly destroyed .... I will gladly aid you in any way I can to keep your command in good shape, but horses are absolutely out of the question. You must find and take them in the country you traverse .... Galbraith was ordered to join you with all the men he had with him, and I will endeavor as far as possible to keep your whole regiment at all times within your immediate control. Now pitch in, Colonel, and help yourself to horses; keep your powder dry and give the guerrillas thunder wherever you can find them.

Meanwhile, in a reorganization of the Cavalry Corps on April 2, 1864, Stokes left the command of the 5th Tennessee, probably unwillingly, and took charge of the post at Carthage. His efforts to return to his first command did not succeed. The regiment moved to the Second Brigade, Brigadier General Alvan C. Gillem's Fourth Division, under Major William J. Clift, son of James Clift who had enlisted Mathews. Colonel Stokes never again actively commanded the regiment he had raised.

For several months after the reorganization, the regiment operated in small detachments under Majors Waters, Clift, and Armstrong through Middle Tennessee. They were reportedly involved in numerous skirmishes at Tullahoma, McMinnville, Sparta, Pulaski, and in Lincoln County. These areas are generally between Nashville and Chattanooga, the home territory of the men of the 5th.

In late August and early September 1864, the 5th Tennessee, under Major General Robert H. Milroy, defended the Nashville & Chattanooga Railroad against a raid by Confederate Major General Joseph 'Fighting Joe' Wheeler. They also engaged the Rebels under Colonel Dibrell at McMinnville, those under Brigadier General John S. Williams on the line from Nashville to Murfreesboro, and others around Triune and Pulaski. General Milroy and the regiment returned to Tullahoma on September 9. The outfit pursued Confederate troops as they withdrew into East Tennessee, but were unable to catch them.

Colonel Stokes continued attempting to regain command of his old outfit. On September 3, 1864, he wrote from Carthage:

... In order to effectually and speedily clear the country of all strag-glers (from Wheeler's forces), I respectfully and earnestly request that the 5th Tennessee Cavalry be ordered to report to me for duty. They can and will do the work. They have been tried, and I have only to point to their achievements for proof of their success in guerrilla warfare. I wish this communication to be laid before His Excellency, Governor Johnson, and shall expect his aid in this mat-ter. It is due to the families of my men that their fathers, brothers, and husbands should be here to protect them ... .

General Milroy recommended on September 19 that Stokes' request be granted. Apparently, it was denied; the regiment was reported to be at Pulaski commanded by Major John F. Armstrong on September 30, 1864, with Brigadier General John C. Starkweather. Lieutenant Colonel William J. Clift was reported as brigade commander of the Second Brigade, Fourth Division. Clift was ordered on Octo-ber 31 to report to Brigadier General John T. Croxton from the Etowah District, who had moved from Chattanooga for the Nashville cam-paign.

One attempt to reorganize the military structure which included the 5th Tennessee never materialized. Major General James H. Wil-son issued orders on November 17, 1864, for the organization of the Sixth Cavalry Division to be commanded by Brigadier General R. W. Johnson. Wilson assigned both the 5th Tennessee Cavalry and the 15th Pennsylvania Cavalry to the Third Brigade. The brigade failed to complete its organization, and the regiments remained separate.

On November 27, the 5th Tennessee moved with General Milroy from Tullahoma to Murfreesboro during the major campaign that culminated in the Battle of Nashville. The utter defeat of Confederate Lieutenant General John B. Hood's Army of the Tennessee by Union forces under Major General John M. Schofield at Franklin on November 30 and under General George H. Thomas at Nashville on December 15 and 16 effectively marked the end of the Confederate Army of the Tennessee, one of the two great armies that the Confed-eracy still had in the field. The 5th Tennessee Cavalry again returned to Tullahoma with Milroy.

Just where Jacob B. Mathews was and what he was doing during the fall of 1864 is not clear. The Company Muster Roll for July-August, under "Remarks," has a note stating "Absent without leave since Sept 18/64." The muster roll for September-October includes the remark, "Absent without leave since Oct 27/64." The muster roll for November-December states "Deserted Wartrace Sept. 23rd 1864. With horse Arms & Ammunition." Wartrace was a small community near Shelbyville. It is not clear what conclusions can be drawn from these records because of the inconsistent and contradictory information found in them.

If Mathews did desert, it would not have been unusual. A report written by General Milroy on January 16, 1865, provides an inside look at the outfit which young Mathews had joined:

When I took command of the defenses of this road, in June, 1864, the 5th Tennessee Cavalry was stationed at this Post. I found it camped outside the picket line of the post, men and officers boarding at private houses, inside and outside the lines. I found that officers and men were absent at home and elsewhere without authority. In fact, I found the regiment utterly void of order and discipline. I at once made it a specialty ... to try and reduce the regiment to some sort of discipline, and worked faithfully, but without any perceptible benefit. I have tried every means known to me to bring about order and efficiency in the regiment, but have not been rewarded with any success, even unto this day.

In fact, the regiment is as far from being an efficient organization as it was in June. The field officers seem to have no conception of their obligations and duties; have no control over their subordinates or men. Officers and men absent themselves without authority whenever they take a notion to visit their homes. The regiment is about 800 strong, and the largest number that can be paraded in camp at any time will not exceed 200. Most of the 600 absentees are unaccounted for.

I have been informed that Colonel Stokes was able to keep the men together, and did hold them under reasonable discipline. I therefore suggest that Colonel Stokes be ordered back to his regiment, because, without him, the regiment is a rabble and entirely worthless to the service. I further suggest that even if Colonel Stokes is ordered back to his regiment, it be sent beyond the state of Tennessee—clear beyond the reach of their homes—as a sure means of making them of service to the Government.

Many of the officers and men live within one or two days' ride of this place, and so long as they are so situated they will be worthless as soldiers. I respectfully request that this regiment be ordered away from my command, and that a regiment of cavalry from some other state be sent in its stead.

General Milroy's petition to send the 5th Tennessee out of the state was not accepted. The regiment received orders on January 26, 1865, to proceed to Fayetteville, Tennessee.

On the same date, according to Mathews' military records in the National Archives, he was "gained" at Tullahoma. A document headed *Returns* has several notes: "Nov. 1864. Loss Sept 23/64, Wartrace. Deserted. Jany 1865. Gained. Jany 26/65 Tullahoma Tenn. Reported deserted by Error. Name appears also as J.B. Mathies." The "gained" note seems to mean that he returned from his desertion. However, since the document adds, "Reported deserted by Error," this statement injects further perplexity into an understanding of Mathews' military experience. Four documents in Mathews' records indicate that he deserted, one states that he returned, and then the same document declares that it was all a mistake!

The last event recorded in the official records about the 5th Tennessee shows that Captain William O. Rickman was commanding the regiment. He was ordered on May 4, 1865, to help the 18th Michigan Cavalry at Huntsville, Alabama, capture or kill a band of Confederates there. The Rebels' commander, though extended the same surrender terms that General-in-Chief U.S. Grant offered Robert E. Lee and Joseph E. Johnston at Appomattox Court House, refused to accept the terms and would not surrender his troops. After that mission, the 5th Tennessee was mustered out of service on August 14, 1865, at Pulaski, Tennessee.

Jacob B. 'Mathis' was present for the entire time, January 26 to August 14. Mathews' records indicate that when he was mustered out, he was eighteen years old (the same age as when he enlisted twenty-two months earlier). He had not been paid since June 30, 1864.

He had drawn $86.77 against his clothing account and owed $38.86. Except for the original $25.00, he had never received any more of the bounty and was due another $75.00; whether or not he ever received it is unknown. He had survived the war without a scratch.

So, long before he ever saw Lincoln County, Territory of New Mexico, J.B. Mathews already had experienced one war: the Civil War. And, his military service was in the Union Army, not the Confederate.

J.B. Mathews' military records: 'Volunteer Enlistment' into the
5th Tennessee Cavalry Regiment, Co. 'M,' October 19, 1863.
(Name shown as 'Mathis'.)
National Archives, Washington, DC.

Declaration of Recruit.

I, *Jacob B. Mathis* desiring to VOLUNTEER as a Soldier in the **Army of the United States**, for the term of THREE YEARS, **Do Declare** that I am *18* years and ____ months of age; that I have never been discharged from the United States service on account of disability or by sentence of court-martial, or by order before the expiration of a term of enlistment; and I know of no impediment to my serving honestly and faithfully as a soldier for THREE YEARS.

GIVEN at *McMinnville* The *19th* day of *October* 186*3*

WITNESS: *Norman Winnell*

Jacob H Mathis

No. 1

Jacob B Mathis
Volunteered at *McMinnville*
October 19th 186*3*
by *James Colys*
Capt Co. ____ Regiment of Tennessee Cav O

____ enlistment; had served in Company (....)
____ Regiment of ____
____ Discharged ____ 186_

Consent in Case of Minor.

I, *John D. Rigsby* *Lawful Guardian* of *Jacob B. Mathis* Do CERTIFY, that I am the ____; that the said *Jacob B. Mathis* is *Eighteen* years of age; and I do hereby freely give my CONSENT to his volunteering as a Soldier in the ARMY OF THE UNITED STATES for the period of THREE YEARS.

GIVEN at *McMinnville*

WITNESS: *Norman Winnell* The *19th* day of *October* 186*3*

John D Rigsby
mark

J.B. Mathews' military records: 'Declaration of Recruit,'
October 19, 1863; 5th Tennessee Cavalry Regiment, Co. 'M.'
(Name shown as 'Mathis'.)
National Archives, Washington, DC.

II

NEW MEXICO TERRITORY

J.B. Mathews returned to his home in Woodbury after the Civil War, but there is some question about how long he stayed there. Joanne McCombs of Roswell, his great-granddaughter, believes his stay was short because he was not well received in his home community due to his Union service. His son, Ernest Mathews, in an article in James Shinkle's 1966 book, *Reminiscences of Roswell Pioneers*, implies that J.B. left Tennessee only months after the war ended in 1865. The account in *An Illustrated History of New Mexico* states that he remained at home until the spring of 1867. This would appear to be the more accurate date for Mathews' departure from Tennessee because it is compatible with the date of the discovery of gold in the Sangre de Cristo Mountains of New Mexico.

Another McMinnville man, Johnny Riley, had been to the gold fields of Colorado and New Mexico and had come home to get married. According to Bess Dow, Riley was the one who started calling Mathews 'Billy,' a nickname by which he was known for the rest of his life. (This Johnny Riley does not appear to be the same man as John H. Riley of Lincoln, New Mexico.) Riley offered to furnish food if Mathews would drive one of his wagons back to Colorado for him. Mathews agreed and made his way to Russell Gulch in Gilpin County, Colorado, where he worked in mining for only a few months.

*   *   *

Following the discovery of gold in 1866, near Elizabethtown, New Mexico Territory, which created a 'gold rush,' Mathews moved there in January 1868 and staked out two claims. In addition, he worked for an English mining company for a few years. During his stay at Elizabethtown he became a member of the local Masonic lodge. However, he tired of the mining business and sold his claims to the company for $2,000. This, and $700 in savings, provided the financial strength which enabled him to seek more beneficial and profitable endeavors elsewhere. Joanne McCombs believes that Mathews and Riley were partners and received equal amounts from the sale of their claims. When Mathews left E'town, Riley apparently stayed there.

According to Ernest Mathews, his father went from Elizabethtown to Fort Stanton, and thence to Lincoln. He was employed for a short time as a clerk for L.G. Murphy & Company, but he did not like being cooped up indoors. He next moved to the Pecos Valley. Some sources indicate that he went directly to the Pecos Valley from Elizabethtown. He said in 1898 that Aaron Wilburn and Milo Pierce "initiated him into the mysteries of the cattle business as it was then in vogue on the frontier." Ernest states that J.B. bought some cattle and drove them to the present site of Roswell, where he and Wilburn combined their small herds and became partners. Ernest gives 1869 as the time of these developments; Nolan and others give later dates, which are more likely accurate.

Mathews and Wilburn established their camp near where the Chaves County Courthouse would later be built, probably some distance east of that location. Their outfit consisted of their herd of cattle, ten saddle horses, eight work horses, two wagons, and two 'government' tents. On the south side of the Río Hondo about where Roswell's East Second Street would later intersect that stream, they built a picket corral that remained there until well into the 1890's.

On one occasion, Mescalero Apache Indians from the Sacramento Mountains to the west stole their horses. According to Ernest, his father and Wilburn rode off from their camp in opposite directions one day. When Mathews got back to the camp about mid-afternoon, he released his horse so it could water at the North Spring River and join the horse herd. He was expecting Wilburn to bring in the horses later so they could catch two of them to stake out for the night, as was their custom. Wilburn discovered that all of them were missing except Mathews' mount. They soon found tracks that indicated Mescaleros had driven off the herd.

Mathews rode to Missouri Plaza, some fifteen miles west on the Hondo, to report the incident. Although there were no settlers left at Missouri Plaza, according to Ernest, a company of soldiers was camping there at the time to prevent Mescaleros from raiding the cattle herds on the Goodnight-Loving Trail along the Pecos River. The soldiers returned with Mathews to his camp. They soon found the Indians' trail, which led east across the Pecos. The troopers caught up with the Mescaleros in the hills east of the Pecos. Several Apaches were killed in the fighting that ensued, and the soldiers successfully retrieved the horses.

Ernest Mathews also writes that J.B. knew Van C. Smith, the recognized founder of Roswell and the one-time partner of Wilburn's brother, Frank. He asserts that Smith had a wife and a daughter who was seven or eight years old and that Mrs. Smith sold meals to passersby for a dollar each. This is a unique claim, because no other account avers that Smith had a family. Aaron Wilburn, in the April 22, 1898, issue of the *Roswell Record* stated that he and J. W. Hulbert started a store at Roswell in 1868 and soon sold out to Smith and Frank Wilburn.

J.B. Mathews' partnership with Aaron Wilburn did not last very long. In the fall of 1873, Mathews filed a claim on land three miles east of Roswell where he farmed and maintained a small herd of cattle. The farm was located at the confluence of the Río Hondo and the Río Berrendo. A colony of beavers had built a dam on the North Spring River about a mile west of Mathews' claim. Mathews plowed a furrow from the dam to his field so he could use the water to irrigate his twenty acres of corn. This was the first irrigation water to be taken out of the Hondo below the mouth of the North Spring River. The corn crop did well until, just as it was about to tassel, a flood washed out the beaver dam. Mathews' corn died, and the next two years saw scant rainfall. When he attempted to file a preemption claim, Mathews learned that his land was a school section, so he let it go back to the

federal government. Twenty-eight-year-old J.B. Mathews found himself looking for better opportunities elsewhere.

Mathews moved his small herd of cattle from the Roswell area to
the Río Peñasco ('Pen-YAHSS-ko,' Spanish for 'rocky bluff') some
seventy-five miles to the southwest in the fall of 1875 (various sources
give dates from 1873 to 1876). Ernest writes that his father was the
first Anglo settler on the Peñasco; this could be true if he moved there
in 1873 or early 1874. According to Lillian Bidal in *Pisacah: A Place
of Plenty* (1996), the first Anglo settlers on the Peñasco were W.W.
Paul, Bill Riley, and William J. Smith, who all moved there in 1874.
However, Ernest gives the date of his father's move as 1875.

Together with Frank Freeman, an Alabaman with a questionable
past, Mathews established a 'squatter' cow camp on land along the
Río Peñasco totalling 640 acres (portions of sections 3 and 10, Range
16 East, Township 16 South) of government land by a large spring
near the mouth of a canyon. Since then, the canyon has been known
as 'Mathews Canyon' and the spring as 'Mathews Spring' or 'Head
Spring.' The origins of the name became obscure over the years and
maps of the area show the canyon as 'Mathew Canyon'; and some
local people call it 'Mathis Canyon.'

In a letter to this author, Lillian Bidal states that the exact site of
Head Spring, which no longer flows, was "in the middle of the river
channel at the point where Mathews Canyon enters the river. Mathews
Canyon is below the mouth of the Little Felix Canyon, below the
place where the trail from the Felix enters the valley." This location is
at the 'head' of that portion of the valley that is designated as the
'Lower Peñasco,' about two miles east (downstream) from the settlement where Bernard and Angie Cleve later established the Elk post
office and store.

Mathews and Freeman built a lean-to for shelter and a corral for
their horses. Mathews was appointed 'forage agent' for the area, presumably by the Army at Fort Stanton.

By early 1877, Mathews and Freeman had already abandoned their
claim and Mathews had moved to Lincoln town. In September of that
year, Mathews turned the forage agent's job over to W.W. Paul and

sold his water rights and improvements to John Henry Tunstall for $700; the land was not his to sell. Freeman apparently made no attempt to collect a share of the money. It is known that Mathews made it a point to avoid or even hide from Freeman. However, Donald Lavash states in *Sheriff William Brady: Tragic Hero of the Lincoln County War* (1986) that it was Freeman, not Mathews, who sold the place to Tunstall.

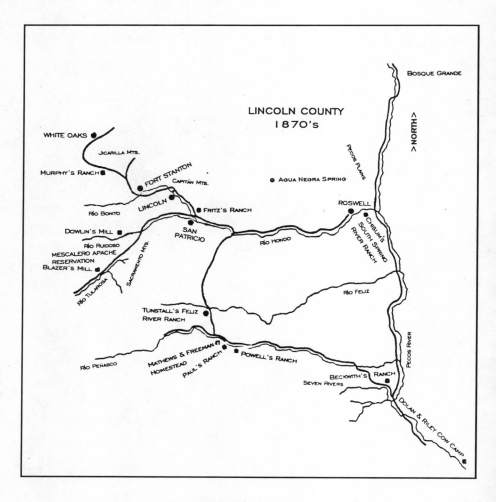

Lincoln County during the 1870s.
Map drawn by the author after Fulton and Bidal.

This review copy of

J. B. 'Billy' Mathews: Biography of a Lincoln County Deputy

by Elvis E. Fleming

is compliments of Yucca Tree Press

It is available at bookstores or may be ordered from the publisher
Yucca Tree Press, 2130 Hixon Drive, Las Cruces, New Mexico 88005-3305
1-800-383-6183 (voice) or 1-505-523-8935 (fax)
$14.95 + $2.00 S&H

III

BILLY MATHEWS AND
THE LINCOLN COUNTY WAR

Following the Civil War, New Mexico Territory found itself caught up in the Cattle Kingdom, along with neighboring Texas and other states and territories. Besides the economic boost brought to the territory by cattlemen, New Mexico also fell heir to all of the violence, myth, and romance that was associated with the Old West. Lincoln County was the most notorious of the centers of frontier violence in New Mexico.

The Territorial Legislature created Lincoln County in 1869 and named it after the recently martyred president, Abraham Lincoln. The size of the county was almost doubled in 1878 so that it constituted some 20-25% of the area of the Territory—all the land between the 32nd and 34th parallels and between the 100th and 104th meridians. This made Lincoln the largest county in the United States. It was bordered by Texas on the east and south.

Hispanic settlers started the little village of *La Placita del Rio Bonito* ('Little Town by the Pretty River') in the early 1850s. When the county was created, the village was designated as the county seat and the name was changed to 'Lincoln.'

The valleys and streams of the Capitán and Sacramento Mountains in the western part of the county attracted early settlers, mostly

Hispanics (both Hispanos and Mexican-Americans). Fort Stanton, near Lincoln, was established in 1855 to protect settlers from the Mescalero Apaches who lived in the Sacramento Mountains. Many former soldiers stayed in the Fort Stanton area and married Hispanic women, assimilating into the local society.

Most of the settlers in the eastern part of the county, on the other hand, were English-speaking 'Anglos' who lived along the Pecos Valley from the Roswell area southward to the vicinity of Seven Rivers. Charles Goodnight and John Chisum drove many thousands of Texas Longhorn cattle up the Pecos Valley on the Goodnight-Loving Trail, bound for the Bosque Redondo Navajo Reservation at Fort Sumner and later for markets as far north as Denver and Cheyenne. Chisum, who came to be known as 'the Cattle King of the Pecos,' established his headquarters first at Bosque Grande and later (1875) at the head of the South Spring River near Roswell.

Violence was rampant in Lincoln County even before it was organized, and it seemed to increase after the county was organized. Indian raids, ethnic conflicts, and just general lawlessness plagued the residents of the huge county. One of the worst episodes was the so-called Horrell War of 1873-74. The five Horrell brothers—Samuel, Thomas, Martin, Benjamin, and Merritt—and their gang of several relatives and hangers-on came to Lincoln County from Lampasas County, Texas, in the spring of 1873 to escape the Texas Rangers and to start a new life. On December 1, they were in Lincoln hurrahing the town as usual; Juan Martínez, the local constable tried to stop them. In the ensuing gun battle, Martínez was killed, along with one of the Horrell gang, Dave Warner. Ben Horrell and L.J. Gylam were wounded, captured, and summarily killed—presumably because the local Hispanics were furious at the way the Horrells had treated them.

The Horrells could not let the locals get away with killing their men, so they attacked an Hispanic wedding on December 20 and killed four or five people. Over the next two months, large posses and equally large groups of Texans engaged each other in violence that took more than a dozen lives. The Horrells then took all the cattle and horses they could round up and headed back to Texas, leaving a posse in their wake. The Horrell War illustrates the violence that served as a prelude to the Lincoln County War as such incidents caused increasing tensions in the county.

One approaches writing about the Lincoln County War with much fear and trembling; virtually every point of fact and interpretation is in dispute. An endless stream of books and articles have been and continue to be written, so any additional account runs the risk of adding new error and embellishing the errors of earlier historians. Further, it is tempting to over-simplify what is actually a very complicated story.

It is not necessary to repeat all the details of the Lincoln County War, but a brief review of that conflict and J. B. Mathews' role in it is appropriate. What follows is a generalized history of the Lincoln County War based on several standard sources on the subject.

Generally speaking, the Lincoln County War was a rivalry between two factions who wanted to control the economy and the politics of the county. They are usually identified as the Murphy-Dolan faction and the Tunstall-McSween faction, although it could be argued that the names of others should be included. The main items of value in Lincoln County were the government contracts to supply beef and staples to the federal installations at Fort Stanton and the Mescalero Apache Indian Agency.

Both factions were composed of businessmen-ranchers, their employees, certain office-holders, and assorted others. Both sides had the support of particular politicians, some Anglos, and some Hispanics. Some previous writers have called it a 'range war' or attempted to categorize the two sides as newcomers against old-timers, Anglos against Hispanics, Irish against English, or Catholics against Protestants. None of these designations holds much water; one might as well call it a war between those who lived on the north side of the street and those who lived on the south side—which is about as valid as the other categories! A more accurate depiction would be: greed for wealth and power versus greed for wealth and power.

Each side owned a big mercantile store in Lincoln. Each faction had a group of gunfighters who were primarily local farmers and cowboys but included some known criminal elements. The Murphy-Dolan gunfighters were more-or-less a sheriff's posse, of which Billy Mathews was the leading deputy. The Tunstall-McSween warriors were originally a constable's posse who had the power to serve arrest warrants that were issued by Justice-of-the-Peace J.B. Wilson. At times, both posses had warrants for the arrest of several members of the other posse! Professor David Townsend of Alamogordo considers the most frightening point of the war to be the excess number of so-called 'lawmen.' In a letter to the author, Dr. Townsend states, "Everyone is carrying legal authority to cover his actions, regardless of how unlawful or outrageous those actions are."

One other general characteristic of the war is that it was fought out in the territorial newspapers. Typically, when an incident caused friction between the factions, a partisan anonymously wrote his version of what happened and sent it to a newspaper in Mesilla, Santa Fe, or Las Vegas. When the account appeared in the paper, someone on the other side responded, also anonymously, and gave the other side's view of the truth to a different newspaper. These accounts provide important information, if the facts can be separated from fabrication or opinion.

Lawrence G. Murphy was the principal economic boss of Lincoln County and pretty much monopolized the county's economy. Born in Ireland, Murphy emigrated to the United States and became a soldier in the U.S. Army. He was discharged in 1866 and became Fort Stanton's sutler, a position he held until 1873. In that year, he established another store in the village of Lincoln. When he was kicked out of Fort Stanton for profiteering, the 'Big Store' in town was his only establishment. He made Emil Fritz a partner and James J. Dolan a junior partner, and the company soon became the dominant factor in the county's economy. The Big Store, or 'the House,' was the only store of any considerable size in the county; and it controlled credit and prices. Murphy also acquired ranching and farming interests. Fritz died in Germany in 1874 when he went there to visit relatives.

Mathews had moved into Lincoln by early 1877 and gone to work for L.G. Murphy & Co. The House had already acquired a reputation for unscrupulous dealing with the public. One such incident was related by Godfrey Gauss and retold in William A. Keleher's book, *Violence in Lincoln County, 1869-1881*. Gauss was a well-known ranch cook. He stated that he had been treated "very badly" by Murphy. Gauss had leased Murphy's brewery for a year, but Murphy declined to put the terms in writing. A couple of months later, after Gauss had produced four hundred gallons of beer, Murphy, Dolan, and Mathews "came with arms" and evicted Gauss, claiming the brewery had been sold. Gauss had no way of moving the beer, so he was forced to sell it to Murphy for forty cents per gallon. Actually, Murphy-Dolan did not pay Gauss the $160.00 they owed him; they paid him only $28.00 and did not sell the brewery, either, Gauss claimed. Mathews' role in the incident is not clear, but Gauss' implication is that he was there in the role of armed 'enforcer.' Mathews' job with the Murphy-Dolan interests placed him in an excellent situation to become familiar with the people and deeply involved in the goings-on in Lincoln County.

Canadian-born Alexander A. McSween and his wife, Susan, arrived in Lincoln in the spring of 1875. McSween, and probably more especially his wife, were very ambitious and desirous of acquiring wealth and power. Their backgrounds are somewhat obscure, but apparently he was educated for both the ministry and the bar. He soon found legal work with Murphy and Dolan.

Another key figure in the Lincoln County scenario was John Henry Tunstall, a wealthy young Englishman who had come to North America to find investments for his family. Judicious and careful, he finally decided to go into the cattle business. He arrived in Lincoln County in the fall of 1876 and acquired land on the Río Feliz, some distance south of Lincoln. He earned the animosity of Murphy and Dolan when he purchased cattle from the widow of Robert Casey at a price higher than the Big Store was offering. (Official federal and state maps show the spelling of the Río Feliz as 'Rio Felix,' feh-LEASE, Spanish for 'happy.' Both spellings are frequently seen, but it seems that the majority of local folks and most Lincoln County War sources prefer the 'Río Feliz' spelling.)

Left: J.B. 'Billy' Mathews (*seated*) and John H. Riley, employees of L.G. Murphy & Co., Lincoln, 1870s. Photo # 200.1. *Right*: J.J. Dolan (*left*) and L.G. Murphy, employers of J.B. Mathews in the 1870s. Photo # 75. *Both photos courtesy: The Robert N. Mullin Collection, Nita Stewart Hale Memorial Library, Midland, Texas.*

Murphy-Dolan store, later the Lincoln County Courthouse. It is shown here as the newly opened Old Lincoln County Courthouse Museum, c. 1936. By Jim Cooley. *Courtesy: Historical Center for Southeast New Mexico, Roswell, photo # 1450A.*

Shortly after Tunstall started his Feliz River Ranch, he decided Murphy and Dolan needed some competition in the mercantile business. He soon established a new store in town: J.H. Tunstall & Company. McSween had no money to buy in, but he planned to earn a partnership in the company by doing legal work for Tunstall. Many people who were opposed to Murphy-Dolan supported the new store. Since there was no bank in Lincoln and Murphy-Dolan controlled credit, Tunstall decided to add a bank to his enterprise. John S. Chisum apparently was a silent partner, and both he and McSween were designated as officers of the bank.

J.J. Dolan & Co. replaced L.G. Murphy & Co. in April 1877. That fall, Billy Mathews used the money he had received from the sale of his water rights and improvements on his claim on the Peñasco to buy a silent (and secret) share in the firm. As Dolan's employee, Mathews clerked in the store. According to Joanne McCombs, he kept the store's books and carried out many other tasks assigned by Dolan, who was happy to have a literate employee.

The Murphy-Dolan store was hurt by the competition from J.H. Tunstall & Co. One sign of their plight was the case of Richard Brewer, who had bought land, equipment, and supplies from Murphy on credit but couldn't seem to produce enough to get out of debt to the company. Alexander McSween advised Brewer that Murphy had no title to the land in the first place. When Brewer started trading with Tunstall, Murphy-Dolan decided to "put the screws to him in their Lincoln County style," according to Fulton in *History of the Lincoln County War* (1968). Consequently, Dolan, along with Billy Mathews and William S. 'Buck' (a.k.a. 'Billy') Morton ('enforcers'?), went well-armed to see Brewer. They told Brewer to pay up or get off the land. Brewer said they could have the land back if they would pay him for the improvements, adding, "I am not hunting a fuss, but I won't run from one."

"If you don't turn the ranch over, you will damn soon find your fuss," Dolan said as a parting shot.

These activities illustrate that Billy Mathews' work for Murphy and Dolan was not all done within the walls of the Big Store. The tasks assigned to him related to every aspect of the broader scope of the business of the company. Mathews' confrontations with Gauss and Brewer imply that it was through such actions that he came to be considered one of the Murphy-Dolan gunfighters.

The brother and sister of Emil Fritz, who also lived in New Mexico, hired McSween in October 1876 to collect the claim on Fritz's life insurance. In August 1877, he told the relatives that he had collected some $7,100.00. Dolan immediately asserted that he should have it all to pay toward the debt owed to the company by Fritz. McSween did not believe him and refused to turn over the insurance money. According to John P. Wilson in *Merchants, Guns, and Money: The Story of Lincoln County and Its Wars*, McSween used the money to build a house for himself and his wife and to purchase goods for Tunstall's store.

The McSweens and Chisum started a well-publicized trip to St. Louis in December 1877. Dolan persuaded Fritz's sister that McSween was leaving the Territory for good and intended to keep the insurance money. He then was able to get the District Attorney in Mesilla, William L. Rynerson, to take action. Rynerson was closely connected with Thomas Catron, the federal district attorney for New Mexico Territory and the acknowledged head of the 'Santa Fe Ring.' The Ring was a group of politicians, lawyers, and some others who operated New Mexico for their own fun and profit.

Catron and Chisum had been antagonists for a long time over other issues, so Catron was happy to have Chisum and McSween arrested when they reached Las Vegas. Catron had clients who held judgments against Chisum. Chisum claimed they were based on his forged signature. Chisum was jailed for about two months; he called it "serving in the Senate."

Susan McSween continued on her trip to St. Louis, while her husband was taken back to Lincoln by Deputy Adolph P. Barrier. He spent a few weeks attending to business in Lincoln, and then Barrier escorted him to Mesilla for a hearing on the Fritz matter. The hearing was inconclusive, but McSween was charged with embezzlement and was placed under an $8,000 writ of attachment. Barrier took McSween back to Lincoln, but McSween persuaded Barrier not to turn him over to Sheriff Brady. McSween 'escaped' and Barrier returned to Las Vegas.

Meanwhile, back in Lincoln, Sheriff William Brady received the writ on February 9 and proceeded to attach all of McSween's property—not just enough to satisfy the writ. Then, on the mistaken belief that McSween and Tunstall were already partners, Brady proceeded to attach Tunstall's store and everything in it.

Tunstall was in Mesilla to accompany McSween back to Lincoln. When they returned on February 10, McSween discovered what the sheriff had done. One of several men who helped the sheriff inventory the store was Billy Mathews.

Tunstall protested to the sheriff that his partnership with McSween had not yet been consummated, but he was able to convince him only that eight horses and mules were not jointly owned. Tunstall shortly had the animals driven to his Río Feliz Ranch. The sheriff then deputized Mathews on February 10 and gave him the responsibility of attaching Alexander McSween's cattle that Brady believed to be pastured on Tunstall's ranch. Mathews and his posse reached the ranch on the 13th.

The details of the events surrounding the death of Tunstall can be pieced together from depositions given by various witnesses. According to Mathews' own testimony, the posse that he took to Tunstall's ranch on February 13 was made up of Robert Beckwith, Thomas Cochran, Pantaleón Gallegos, Thomas Green, George Hindman, John Hurley, George Kitt, Charles Kruling, Charles Marshall, Ramón Montoya, Buck Morton, J.W. Olinger, Sam Perry, and Manuel 'The Indian' Segovia.

Deputy U.S. Marshal Robert Widenmann testified that the posse also included Andrew Roberts, Jessie Evans, Frank Baker, and Tom Hill (a.k.a. Chelson). Evans, Baker, and Hill were known gunfighters who had threatened to kill Widenmann. When the posse approached the Tunstall ranch house, Widenmann saw that the three were in the group, so he came outside and told them to stop where they were, some fifty yards from the house. He asked Mathews to come forward and state his business. Mathews replied that he was a deputy sheriff and was there to attach McSween's cattle. Widenmann told him that McSween had no cattle there but if they found any they could take them.

Dick Brewer, Tunstall's foreman, told Mathews that the posse could round up the cattle if they wanted to; if Mathews believed any of the cattle were McSween's, he could leave someone there to watch them until the matter was settled in court.

Widenmann announced that he was arresting Jessie Evans, claiming to have a federal warrant. However, Brewer and the others present refused to help him for fear of retaliation by Murphy, Dolan, and Riley. Mathews told Widenmann that the reason Evans was there was to find out if Widenmann had a warrant for him. While Mathews was talking, Baker said to Roberts, "What the hell's the use of talking? Pitch in and fight and kill the s.o.b." After some tense moments, Brewer offered to have Godfrey Gauss, the cook, feed the posse.

Sheriff Brady later stated that "... the threatening attitude of the armed men around him convinced my deputy that the destruction of himself and party would speedily follow any attempt to enforce the attachment." Mathews announced that he would return to town for further instructions regarding the cattle. At the urging of the Tunstall men, he conceded that he would bring just one man with him when he returned.

Widenmann, William H. 'Kid' 'Billy' Bonney, and Fred Waite rode several miles with Mathews and a couple of his men, while the rest of the posse went to Paul's ranch on the Peñasco. Mathews asked Widenmann if Tunstall's supporters would object if the posse attached Tunstall's cattle. His reply was that there would be no objection if the cattle were left on the ranch, but if the plan—as some feared—were to drive them to the Mescalero agency and butcher them, then "we would do all that was in our power to defeat them."

Sheriff Brady increased the posse to "about twenty-four of the best citizens procurable." One of the controversies concerning the first posse was the belief that it included men who were wanted by the U.S. Marshal. Brady maintained that the allegation was not true and told Mathews verbally and in written form that he was not to include any such men in the second posse:

> Lincoln, N.M. Feb. 15th, 1878
> J.B. Mathews,
>   Deputy Sheriff
> Dear Sir: You must not by any means call on or allow to travel with your posse any person or persons who are known to be outlaws. Let your Mexicans round up the cattle and protect them with the balance. Be firm and do your duty according to law and I will be responsible for your acts.
>   I am sir, Respectfully yours,
>   William Brady, Sheriff, Lincoln Co.

Mathews testified that he raised a part of the second posse in Lincoln. He listed the names of the Lincoln posse members as follows: James J. Dolan (who joined the group later), Pantaleón Gallegos, George Hindman, John Hurley, Felipe Mes, Ham Mills, Ramón Montoya, Thomas Moore, Pablo Pino y Pino, Andrew Roberts, Manuel 'Indian' Segovia, and E.H. Wakefield. On Thursday, February 14, they proceeded to the ranch of former sheriff A.H. 'Ham' Mills on the Río Ruidoso.

Mathews' account apparently includes an extra day; he stated that on the 15th, the posse rode to Turkey Springs and spent the night. The following day, Friday, they arrived at W.W. Paul's Half-Circle P Ranch on the Peñasco in the afternoon. Actually, Friday would have been the 15th. Some of the events that Mathews described as being on separate days must have taken place on the same day.

On Saturday, uninvited guests moved in with the posse: Jessie Evans and Tom Hill. Evans claimed that he was there to recover one or more of his horses from Kid Bonney. The next day, Frank Baker and John Long 'Rivers' also came in and stayed. Mathews did not consider them to be a part of the posse and ordered them away. However, it is clear that they stayed put.

While they were at Paul's, additional possemen from Seven Rivers in the Pecos Valley joined them. Mathews had sent Telesfor López there to instruct Buck Morton, who had charge of Dolan's cow camp on the Pecos, to raise a posse. According to Robert M. Utley in *Billy the Kid: A Short and Violent Life* (1989), those from Seven Rivers who were with Morton were Robert W. Beckwith, Thomas Cochran, Thomas Green, George Kitt, Charles 'Dutch Charley' Kruling, Charles Marshall, J.W. Olinger, Sam Perry, and Charles Wolz.

The expanded posse set out from Paul's ranch for the seven-mile ride to Tunstall's Feliz River Ranch on Monday, February 18. Mathews informed his men that 'Dutch Martin' Martz had told him that Dick Brewer, Tunstall's foreman, would not resist the posse. Martz was one of the managers of Tunstall's place at Mathews Spring on the Peñasco. However, they did expect trouble from Robert Widenmann.

Meanwhile, Tunstall had been trying, without much success, to recruit men to help him fight the Dolan forces as embodied in Mathews' posse. He heard rumors that the posse had grown to forty-three and that the posse had plans to kill him and all his men and seize his cattle. He tried in vain to get help from the Chisums, but John was still "serving in the Senate" in Las Vegas. His brothers, James and Pitser, were unwilling to commit. Tunstall rushed home to the ranch on Sunday the 17th, where he devised a plan. The strategy called for William McCloskey, a friend of some in the posse, to go to Paul's ranch and tell Mathews that Tunstall would not endanger the lives of his men by resisting the attachment of his cattle. Also, McCloskey was to ask Martz to accompany Mathews to count the cattle in Tunstall's behalf. Godfrey Gauss, the cook, would be left to face the posse while Tunstall and all the rest of his men would take off early the next morning for Lincoln.

When Tunstall's crew left the ranch, they drove Tunstall's six prize horses, two of Dick Brewer's, and the one or more of Kid Bonney's which were keeping Jessie Evans and the other criminals on the scene. Those accompanying Tunstall were Bonney, Dick Brewer, Henry Brown, John Middleton, Fred Waite, and Widenmann. Brown shortly left the group and headed south. About ten miles north of the ranch, Waite followed the road in a buckboard while the others took a short-cut.

Mathews said, "We went to the ranch carefully, one party in front of the house and the other from the rear, myself and Roberts being the party in front. We found there was no one there except Gauss and I think 'Dutch Martin.'" He asked Gauss where Brewer and the others were, and Gauss told him that they had started for Lincoln with the horses.

According to Gauss, the possemen helped themselves to food. Gauss, in his somewhat heavy accent, later testified that Mathews asked him, "Why not some one remain to turn over the property?" Gauss told Mathews that Martz was coming to handle that. Mathews' men then proceeded, Gauss stated, to shoe three or four horses with Tunstall's materials. Further, Gauss quoted Mathews as saying, "If only Jim (Dolan) was here—I have a notion to send after them and bring them back."

Gauss claimed that Dolan did show up about that time. Dolan seemed to be calling the shots after he arrived. He chose the men to go after Tunstall's party and bring them back, assuming they could catch up with them before they reached Lincoln. Mathews' testimony was that "I then deputized Morton and selected a party to go with him after the horses and bring them back, and in case there was any resistance to arrest the men and bring them back too." If they went to Lincoln, Mathews told Morton, he was to follow them and tell the sheriff to attach the horses.

Morton's subposse consisted of fourteen men. Mathews protested when Baker, Evans, and Hill prepared to go along; but Evans asserted that Bonney had his horse and that he had a right to get it back. The three outlaws followed behind the posse. Frederick Nolan, in *The Lincoln County War: A Documentary History* (1993), asserts that Mathews later lied under oath when naming the subposse, purposely omitting the names of the outlaws. However, Mathews had told those worthies to leave, had protested their accompanying the subposse, and didn't consider that they were part of the subposse. One could speculate that Mathews considered it hazardous to his own hide to protest too vigorously against the presence of Evans, Baker, and Hill.

As the long day in the saddle neared its end, Tunstall and his men crossed a ridge and descended a canyon that would lead them to the Río Ruidoso. When those out front scared up a flock of turkeys,

Widenmann and Brewer took off up a hillside after the birds. Tunstall stayed with the horses on the trail, while Middleton and Bonney poked along some distance behind.

Bringing up the rear, as Middleton and Bonney crossed the ridge they spotted Morton's subposse racing up behind them on the trail. Middleton took off to warn Tunstall, while Bonney headed for Widenmann and Brewer. When the subposse crested the ridge, they saw Widenmann, Brewer, and Bonney and began firing. The three headed for cover higher up the slope. Middleton yelled for Tunstall to follow him, but Tunstall seemed to be flustered and agitated in the swirl of a rapidly-deteriorating situation. Tunstall apparently couldn't hear or understand Middleton. When Middleton continued to call out to Tunstall, Tunstall's only reply was "What, John? What, John?" Middleton joined the others as they bolted for the safety of cover.

The men in the subposse stopped their pursuit of Brewer and the others when they saw Tunstall with the horses on the trail. According to Buck Morton, he ordered Tunstall to give up. Rather than surrender, Tunstall, now about three hundred feet away from the trail in a stretch of brushy timber, jerked out his six-shooter and fired twice at the deputies. Morton and the outlaw interlopers, Jessie Evans and Tom Hill, were the only ones who were close enough to see Tunstall. They all fired back at the young Englishman, hitting him in the head and the chest. For good measure, they also shot his horse. Mathews' fears were realized: sure enough, two of the outlaws that he had not wanted along were the very ones, along with Morton, who did the actual killing of Tunstall.

The sound of gunfire from the trail reached Tunstall's men just as they reached the cover of some scrub timber and big rocks. Middleton exclaimed, "They've killed Tunstall!

Chief Deputy Mathews' report stated:

Morton returned (to the Tunstall ranch house) at about 2 A.M. the next day (February 19) and reported that he caught up with the horses about 30 miles away and that Tunstall resisted and fired at him and that he returned the fire and Tunstall was killed. That the resistance was made by Tunstall while he was reading the attachment to him, and that he notified Tunstall that if he would throw up his hands he would not be hurt, instead of which Tunstall fired at him, that he fired back killing Tunstall.

This became the official version of what transpired, although none of those in the Tunstall camp believed it. The federal investigator who looked into the death of English citizen Tunstall, Frank Warner Angel, concluded that "... John H. Tunstall was murdered in cold blood and was not shot in attempting to resist an officer of the law." Angel partially blamed the killing on the fact that Morton had allowed "these notorious out-laws to accompany him."

The distraction of Tunstall's killing seems to have caused most sources to make no further mention of the attachment that Mathews and his posse went to Tunstall's ranch to serve. In fact, the remainder of the posse went into camp about 500 yards from Tunstall's house and proceeded to attach the cattle and horses on the ranch. According to Mathews' report they attached 188 cattle branded "S fresh with an X," including 110 cows, 31 yearling calves, 45 two-year-old calves, and two bulls. Also, they attached 102 head of cattle that were branded "X" and some had other brands as well; these comprised 55 cows, 25 yearlings, and 22 two-year-olds. Further, included in the attachment were 18 cows with the Arrow-Slash brand, three bulls branded "Slash" on the side, and eight cattle with indistinguishable brands. Finally, the posse attached eight cow ponies and horses, a set of harness, two blacksmith anvils, a crowbar, and a long-handled shovel, Mathews reported.

An examination of Tunstall's store books showed that he had a list of uncollectible notes. According to Nolan, "... virtually all of them (were) for goods advanced against future harvests ... a veritable roll-call of those who had either fled the county or been rendered unable to meet their obligations by events." Curiously, listed among Tunstall's debtors was Murphy-Dolan employee J.B. Mathews.

Tunstall's death is generally considered to be the beginning of the Lincoln County War, following about two years of increasing tensions between the factions.

*   *   *

One of the cowboys on Tunstall's ranch was a young man usually called 'Kid' because he looked so young. His real name was probably Henry McCarty, but he had used several names; at this time he called himself 'William H. Bonney.' Today he is known the world over as 'Billy the Kid.' Bonney, as well as other Tunstall hands, vowed to avenge their employer's death. The local constable, Atanacio Martínez, deputized Brewer, the Kid, and several others to create a constable's posse that later turned into a sort of vigilante group known as 'The Regulators.'

Sheriff Brady was not disposed to arrest his own posse for Tunstall's death—a legal act, as far as he was concerned. He sent a letter to Thomas Catron giving his view of what had happened. Catron showed the letter to Governor Samuel B. Axtell and asked that he request President Rutherford B. Hayes to send federal troops to help the civil officers in Lincoln County. Axtell telegraphed the request to the president. He also went to Lincoln, where on March 9 he spent three hours, all in the company of Dolan, investigating the situation. He then authorized Colonel George Purington, commander of Fort Stanton, to help Brady keep the peace.

The Regulators worked hard on their vow to kill the men responsible for Tunstall's death, dispatching Morton and Baker (and McCloskey in the process) to their reward on March 9 at Agua Negra Spring. According to Nolan, Bonney attempted to gun down Mathews on March 29, but failed.

Sheriff Brady was their next target. It has been customary to consider Brady a Murphy-Dolan henchman, and it is true that when carrying out his official duties, he tended to favor Murphy-Dolan. However, as his biographer, Donald Lavash, has so ably shown, Brady was not Murphy-Dolan's puppet.

J.B. Mathews had a close scrape with death when The Regulators assassinated Brady and Deputy George Hindman in Lincoln on April 1, 1878. On that Monday morning, the sheriff, Hindman, Mathews, George Peppin, and John Long were walking along the town's only

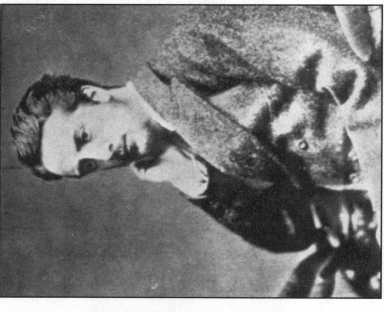

Left: Sheriff William Brady named Billy Mathews as his chief deputy to attach Alexander McSween's cattle which were thought to be pastured on Tunstall's ranch. Brady was assassinated by The Regulators, April 1, 1878. Photo # 30. *Right*: John Henry Tunstall, whose killing on February 18, 1878, started the Lincoln County War. By Henry Dixon & Son, Victoria, BC, 1875. Photo # 216.

Both photos courtesy: The Robert N. Mullin Collection, Nita Stewart Haley Memorial Library, Midland, TX.

street. When the men reached the front of Tunstall's store, The Regulators began firing from the corral gate behind the store. The sheriff was killed instantly and Hindman was mortally wounded. After the sheriff fell, Bonney ran out and grabbed the sheriff's rifle on the premise that the sheriff had confiscated it from him. Mathews, who had taken refuge in the Sisneros house and was watching from the window, fired his .44 calibre 1873 Winchester saddle carbine at the Kid and wounded his left thigh. Joanne McCombs stated that according to family legend, Bonney hid in an Hispanic woman's house and escaped by wearing her dress and *rebozo* as a disguise. The Kid later told Susan McSween that he was shooting at Mathews, not the sheriff, according to Nolan. The Regulators' ambush of the sheriff cost them much public support and was a principal turning point in the conflict.

Peppin hurried to Fort Stanton and soon Colonel Purington and about twenty-five soldiers arrived in Lincoln. According to McSween's later testimony, Peppin talked Purington into allowing the deputies to search McSween's house for arms. Peppin and the posse, McSween said:

> ... went to the house to search, I forbade them to enter unless they had a warrant for that purpose. I said these words on that occasion: "Peppin, you know that you are not an officer, but were you, you can't search without a warrant for that purpose." Whereupon Mathews replied, "We can't? Aye, we'll show you what we can do!" Then Peppin replied that Col. Purington gave him permission to search the house.

The colonel then arrested McSween, Widenmann, David Shield (Mrs. McSween's sister's husband), George Robinson, and George Washington. Robinson and Washington were former Buffalo Soldiers who were employed by the McSweens. The arresting soldiers took them all to the guardhouse at Fort Stanton.

On April 4, Andrew 'Buckshot' Roberts, who had been in the posse that killed Tunstall, rode his mule up to Blazer's Mill where The Regulators were eating. Many explanations have circulated as to why The Regulators and/or Roberts were at the mill, so exactly what they were up to is uncertain. Kid Bonney had already rejoined The Regulators, the wound inflicted by Mathews a few days earlier not being serious. A gunfight ensued. Roberts was mortally wounded, but he managed to kill Brewer and wound Billy Bonney, John Middleton, and George Coe in the battle.

The Lincoln County Grand Jury met from April 8 through April 24, 1878. The many indictments they handed down were mostly against the Murphy-Dolan faction. For the killing of Tunstall, the jury indicted Jessie Evans and some of his gang members who actually were not even with the subposse that killed Tunstall. The jury also indicted Dolan and Mathews as accessories to murder in Tunstall's death. Morton and Hill were both dead by the time the jury met.

Another incident in which Mathews was a participant was the ambush of The Regulators on April 29, 1878. Mathews and Peppin, maintaining that they were still deputy sheriffs, traveled from Lincoln to the Seven Rivers area with Dolan and Hurley. There they organized a posse of about twenty local men. They wanted to 'help' Sheriff John Copeland, whom they suspected of being a McSween adherent, to arrest The Regulators for killing Brady, Hindman, Baker, Morton, and McCloskey. On the return to Lincoln, the so-called 'Seven Rivers Warriors' waylaid The Regulators at the Fritz Ranch on the Río Bonito; and three of The Regulators—Frank McNab, Ab Saunders, and Frank Coe—rode into the trap. The sheriff's men killed the leader, McNab, and mortally wounded Saunders. Coe surrendered.

The following day, the Seven Rivers posse surrounded the Ellis & Son store in Lincoln in a fracas that historian Robert M. Utley has dubbed the 'Battle of Lincoln.' Captain George W. Smith arrived with troops from Fort Stanton and arrested the Dolan men. According to 'Soapweed' in a letter to the *Cimarron News and Press*, the Dolan followers had the run of the fort and were not even disarmed until the second day. The anonymous writer was particularly incensed at J.B. Mathews: "With the accusation of double murder against him, J.B. Mathews was allowed to go to Murphy's ranch after cattle to fill the beef contract at the Post, and this without the knowledge or consent of the sheriff."

These examples illustrate how Mathews was usually in the thick of things in the county during the days of strife between the Murphy-Dolan and Tunstall-McSween factions. After the federal investigator, Frank Warner Angel, made his report in November 1878, it became traditional for historians to describe the Murphy-Dolan element as the 'bad guys' and the Tunstall-McSween group as the 'good guys.' Modern historians, such as Frederick Nolan and Robert Utley, have judged the principal characters on both sides to be more-or-less equally unrighteous. It was dangerous to try to maintain neutrality, although most of those involved were average folks who happened to get caught up in the intrigues of the leaders. It could be concluded, for example, that Billy Mathews tried to make the best of a bad situation by attending, along with other Dolan partisans, the church services held by the Reverend Dr. Taylor F. Ealy on June 23, 1878, at McSween's house.

The Five-Day Battle in Lincoln, July 15-19, 1878, climaxed the Lincoln County War. McSween recruited an 'army' of forty-five to sixty men that entrenched themselves around the town in preparation for an inevitable showdown. This caught Sheriff Peppin off guard, but he soon amassed a group of deputies and possemen to confront the McSween men.

Billy Mathews' part in the battle and its outcome were not especially visible nor significant. He entered the *torreon*, or 'Indian tower,' along with the sheriff and four other men at the start of the battle. Their supplies were brought over from the house next door, which was the residence of Saturnino Baca, a Dolan partisan; both the tower and the house were owned by McSween. Baca was ordered by the outraged McSween to get out immediately. Baca's wife had just given birth, and he did not want to move her and the baby. He sent word to Fort Stanton, which he had at one time commanded, to send protection. Lieutenant Colonel Nathan Dudley, who had taken over as commander on April 5, was unable to comply but sent the post surgeon to see if he could help. An agreement apparently was reached that

The Torreon played a pominment role in the Five-Day Battle in
Lincoln, July 1878. *Above*: Torreon in Lincoln before restoration,
c. 1934. Photo # 1275. *Below*: Torreon after restoration by the
Chaves County Archaeological and Historical Society, January 1935.
Photo #1450E by Jim Cooley.
Both photos courtesy: Historical Center for Southeast New Mexico, Roswell.

neutral soldiers should be placed in the torreon, but nothing was actually done to solve the dispute. A deputy sheriff went to McSween's house with warrants for him and The Regulators there with him. The McSween faction fired at the deputy so he withdrew.

The sheriff's forces were reinforced by the arrival of men from the Seven Rivers area, including Jessie Evans and Buck Powell. The 'battle' was pretty much a stand-off for three days, as each side fired occasionally at the other from their hiding places. Peppin asked for help from the military, but the Fort Stanton commander was obliged to decline because federal troops were "... circumscribed by laws and orders ..." at that point in time from helping local officials. When a trooper with the missive for the sheriff was fired upon, the sheriff told Colonel Dudley that McSween's gunfighters had done the shooting. Dudley held a board of inquiry at the fort, which decided that military intercession was now warranted.

On Friday morning, July 19, Dudley came to town with thirty-five soldiers, a cannon, and a Gatling gun. The big weapons intimidated the McSween men who were fortified in the Montaño and Ellis stores. They abandoned their posts and attempted to approach the McSween house from the Río Bonito, but were driven away by the sheriff's men. They headed north and disappeared from the scene, depleting McSween's army by about two-thirds.

McSween protested the use of the military in a note to Dudley. Dudley pretended to misunderstand the note and replied in an arrogant, mocking manner that no soldiers were surrounding the house and that he did not want to negotiate with McSween. Desperate, Susan McSween went out to talk with Dudley. He rejected her appeal, but he did allow the women and children to come out of the McSween house and the Ealy family to get out of the Tunstall store building unharmed.

The sheriff's men set the McSween house on fire in the early afternoon on Friday. The blaze burned from room to room all afternoon, forcing the occupants to retreat before it. At dusk, the McSween party was forced to try to make a break from the burning house. Five men, one of whom was Billy the Kid, dashed out first to draw the attention of the sheriff's men while McSween escaped. Harvey

Morris was killed; the Kid and the others made it. By the time McSween decided to come out, the sheriff's men were already through firing at the escapees.

Someone in the McSween party yelled that they would surrender, and Bob Beckwith and three other deputies came into the back yard. At that point, a shot from the house killed Beckwith. The others fired back; and, before it was over, McSween and all of his men were shot down. Only one McSween partisan, a teenager named Yginio Salazar, survived. Critically wounded, Salazar played dead until he could slip away for medical help.

Although there is no explicit record, it is believed that Billy Mathews helped the sheriff during the entire Five-Day Battle. When the fighting ended, the sheriff's men celebrated by dancing and singing in the street. They also plundered Tunstall's store.

The climactic battle did not bring peace. The war did gradually subside, but disorder in Lincoln County escalated over the next few months. In the absence of competent law enforcement, several new outlaw elements were attracted to the county. The turmoil in Lincoln continued to increase toward the end of 1878. In December, Billy Bonney and a gang of former McSween supporters rode in from Fort Sumner and took over the town. Mathews, Dolan, and Long sought protection from the attackers by rushing to Fort Stanton. Incomplete court records show the Kid was jailed for a short while as a consequence of this incident.

On the first anniversary of Tunstall's death, Dolan, Mathews, Evans, and newcomer Billy Campbell of the Murphy-Dolan faction got together with the Kid, Tom O'Folliard, and Yginio Salazar of The Regulators in Lincoln to sign a truce. There were some anxious moments between Evans and the Kid at first. After a parley, the negotiators signed a pact and decided to seal it with a few drinks. Later, as the drunken party came out of one of the saloons, they met Huston Chapman, the lawyer whom Susan McSween had hired to settle her late husband's estate and that of John Henry Tunstall. In the ugly scene that followed, someone shot and killed Chapman. Likely what happened, according to Nolan, is that Dolan accidentally fired his weapon into the ground. The noise startled Campbell, who had his weapon pointed at Chapman's chest, causing him to squeeze off a round at close range.

Because of Chapman's death, Governor Lew Wallace finally came to Lincoln to investigate. Even before he arrived in the village, Wallace issued orders to Colonel Edward Hatch, the new commander of the U.S. Military District of New Mexico, to arrest those he believed to have killed Chapman. "I have information that William Campbell, J.B. Mathews and Jesse Evans were of the party engaged in the killing of the late H.J. Chapman ... ." The three wanted men were at the Carrizozo Ranch with Dolan at the time. Soldiers took them into custody and placed them in the guardhouse at Fort Stanton. The military also arrested Dolan shortly afterward. Wallace believed the prison quarters at Fort Stanton were unsafe and took measures to have the men transferred to Fort Union, but later changed his mind. Campbell and Evans escaped on March 19, so security was tightened lest the others should do likewise. Dolan and Mathews were incarcerated at the fort until the Grand Jury met the following month.

Governor Wallace had issued his amnesty proclamation on November 13, 1878, offering immunity to those who would stop the violence and tell what they knew in a court of law. The Lincoln County Grand Jury handed down many indictments in the spring term of 1879 to add to those that they had imposed the previous year. Despite Governor Wallace's belief that Mathews was one of Chapman's killers, the Grand Jury indicted only Dolan and Campbell for murder and Evans as an accessory, completely passing over Mathews.

The 1878 Grand Jury had indicted Mathews as an accessory in the killing of Tunstall. Mathews and others who had been indicted for various actions since the start of the war opted to plead "not guilty" and ask for a change of venue instead of accepting amnesty. About May 1, 1879, the court granted a change of venue to Socorro County for Mathews, Peppin, Thomas B. 'Buck' Powell, and a number of others. However, Mathews and some of the others eventually, in the words of Fulton, "... went to the trouble of having their offenses purged away by accepting what their lawyers, Catron and Thornton, called the 'Wallace amnesty.'" Mathews was not through with Billy the Kid, though.

*   *   *

Pat Garrett, the new sheriff of Lincoln County, caught up with the Kid near Fort Sumner in December 1880. Stu Pritchard, in *Recuerdos de Ante Años* (1971), incorrectly indicates that Billy Mathews was Garrett's deputy. Bonney was put on trial in April 1881, for the murder of Sheriff Brady. The district attorney moved the Kid's trial to Mesilla on a change of venue.

The principal witness for the prosecution was none other than Billy Mathews. According to Jacobsen, Mathews testified that Brady was ambushed, showing premeditation. He also swore that Bonney ran out from his hiding place, showing that he was in on a conspiracy, regardless of whether or not he fired the actual shot that killed the sheriff. That was enough to convict the Kid. On April 13, 1881, the judge pronounced sentence: the Kid was to be hanged in Lincoln on May 13.

Seven men guarded Bonney on the long wagon trip back to Lincoln from Mesilla, five of whom were special deputies for this assignment. Three of the five were known to be unfriendly toward the Kid: Mathews; John Kinney, the king of Southern New Mexico rustlers; and 'Pecos Bob' Olinger, who was to meet his Maker two weeks later when Bonney escaped. Kinney sat beside the Kid, while Mathews and Olinger sat across facing them in the wagon. They left Mesilla on April 16. Sheriff Garrett met them at Fort Stanton on the 21st, assumed custody of the prisoner, and led the entourage into Lincoln.

Then, as the whole world knows, Billy the Kid made his famous last escape on April 28, 1881, from the new Lincoln County Courthouse—the original Murphy-Dolan store building. Billy Mathews had no further connection with the factional strife in Lincoln County after he helped escort Billy Bonney back to Lincoln. However, Billy the Kid went to the Peñasco Valley looking for Mathews and Buck Powell after he escaped from the courthouse. According to Utley, the Kid stole a horse at Las Tablas and went to the Peñasco. He spent some time with his old friend, John Meadows, who "... suspected that the Kid had come to the Peñasco to do away with Billy Mathews ... ." The Kid actually denied that he would hurt Mathews if he saw him, but Meadows didn't believe him. Rumors abounded that the Kid did, in fact, gun down Mathews. According to Jacobsen, "Mathews experienced the peculiar pleasure of reading his own admiring obituaries when the papers reported that the Kid had gunned him down on the outskirts of Lincoln." The papers—to paraphrase Mark Twain—grossly exaggerated the reports of Mathews' death! Ernestine Chesser Williams in *Treasures of History II: Chaves County Vignettes* (1991) relates that the Kid did find Powell, but failed to recognize him.

Sheriff Pat Garrett tracked the Kid down and shot him to death at Fort Sumner on July 14, 1881.

Fulton summarizes, "Mathews was not by nature a man of violence. As hostilities subsided he quickly disassociated himself from his connection with the feud ... ." *An Illustrated History of New Mexico* gives Mathews much credit in its very confused and inaccurate account of the Lincoln County War:

> The course which Mr. Mathews followed during this trying period was a most courageous and commendable one. He fearlessly discharged the duties devolving upon him, counting not the personal cost, and it was largely through his efforts that the matter was terminated so as to preserve the interests of those who were on the side of right.

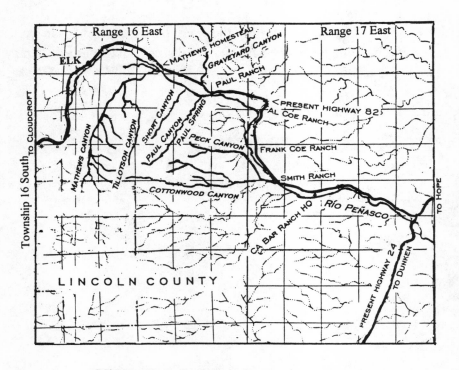

Middle Río Peñasco Valley during the 1880s.
Map drawn by the author, after Bidal and official state maps.

IV

RANCHING ON THE PEÑASCO

J.J. Dolan, in partnership with William Rynerson, acquired Tunstall's Feliz River Ranch after the Lincoln County War. Lillian Bidal states, in her monumental history of the Peñasco Valley, *Pisacah: A Place of Plenty* (1996), that Dolan acquired that property and others through homestead filings by Mathews, Dolan, and members of Dolan's wife's family. Dolan employed Mathews as range manager there in the early 1880's.

Except for the events related to Billy the Kid's trial, accounts differ about Mathews' activities following Chapman's death. For example, a petition signed by residents of the Peñasco Valley in July 1880 includes the signature of J.B. Mathews, which would suggest that he was already living there. The petition asked the county commissioners to create a new precinct and provide law officers for that portion of the county. In another example, Utley states that Billy the Kid went to the Peñasco after his escape in late April 1881 "... to do away with Billy Mathews, who had a ranch nearby." Further, Bidal states that Mathews was employed on the Dolan Ranch on the Río Feliz "for several years as a range manager." All of this indicates that Mathews left Lincoln within a year or so of Chapman's death. However, evidence also shows that he lived on Dolan's ranch on the Feliz at first and didn't move back to the Peñasco until 1884.

In a 1961 letter in Ernestine Chesser Williams' *Echoes Break the Silence* (1987), Ernest Mathews claims that his father was persuaded by Mescalero Apaches to use the Flying H brand to mark Dolan's herds. The Mescaleros promised they would never surreptitiously butcher a Dolan beef if the cattle wore the Flying H brand. The ranch eventually took both the brand and the name. Interestingly, another version of this story, related by Joanne McCombs, Mathews' great-granddaughter, is that the Apaches' instructions applied to the CA Bar brand instead of the Flying H.

Another interesting story involving Mescaleros was related by Richard 'Dick' R. Armstrong, Mathews' great-grandson. On one occasion Billy needed to sleep but there were Mescaleros prowling about the vicinity. He was worried that the Indians might steal his horse, so he tied one end of his rope to his wrist and the other end to his horse. He then was able to sleep; but when he awoke, the rope had been cut and the horse was nowhere to be seen.

Mathews filed a homestead claim in 1881 on a quarter-section of his squatter's claim on the Peñasco (the one he had sold to Tunstall), according to Bidal. Department of the Interior officials rejected the claim as fraudulent. Thomas C. 'Tom' Tillotson later filed on the same homestead and perfected the claim (the log house he built there was still being occupied in 1997). Mathews continued working for Dolan on the Feliz. However, life was soon to change for Billy Mathews: he was about to take a bride.

James T. and Margaret Bates, originally of Tupelo, Mississippi, moved their family onto the Lower Peñasco in 1881. Their son, Ralph, in an interview with Fred Griffin in 1937, related some family background which was reprinted in *Artesia: Heart of the Pecos*, by Lela and Rufus Waltrip (1979). Ralph was born in Tupelo in 1865; his sister, Dora Matilda (or Mathilda), was born there on August 20, 1867. James Bates moved his family to Texas in 1869, settling at first near Brady. Other descendants related that the Bateses were known as 'rawhiders,' a designation of poor people who not only ate the venison of the deer they hunted; they also wore clothes and shoes made from the hides. By the late 1870's, Ralph said, they were in Concho County. From there they drove their cattle to Seven Rivers in the Pecos Valley of New Mexico Territory in 1879. By June 1881, they had sold their land in Texas and proceeded to move all of their farming equipment and household furnishings to Seven Rivers.

While the elder Bates scouted the Sacramento and Guadalupe Mountains for a place to establish a ranch, Ralph helped to watch the family herd in the Pecos Valley in the area from Seven Rivers to just south of present Carlsbad. The cattle of Buck Powell, Gordon Nash, and another man by the name of Williams were also in the same area. Ralph was assigned to Rat Nest Line Camp, which was at the mouth of Dark Canyon.

James Bates decided on a claim located just below Mathews Spring, an unperfected homestead claim which he purchased from Martin 'Buck' Blevins. Bidal describes the claim as being "wedged between Tom Tillotson's Head Springs homestead and timber claims." The Bates family then moved onto their new claim in September 1881.

Ralph told an interesting story about their first night on the new place: "... We necked our work steers together and turned them out to graze. The next morning one yoke of oxen was gone. I saddled a pony and overtook them at the Buck Powell Springs; they were headed for their old range at Seven Rivers. The cottonwood switch with which I whipped them back up the trail was worn to a short stub when I got home. I stuck the frayed stub in the mud of the ditch bank, where it took root and grew. It is growing there today (1937)—the big cottonwood just west of the house at the Cleve farm."

Billy Mathews met the Bates family, which now included four more children born in Texas (three more would be born to them in New Mexico). Mathews was particularly interested in the beautiful teenaged Dora Matilda. Although Dora was not quite sixteen years old and was some twenty years younger than Mathews, they were married on July 11, 1883. The wedding was performed by Justice-of-the-Peace Robert Dickson and witnessed by Albert and Mollie Coe. Al Coe was a brother of Frank Coe, who had been a leading member of Mathews' old Lincoln County War nemesis, The Regulators. Both Al and Frank Coe had ranches on the Peñasco.

There is an impression in some quarters that Mathews had been married in the 1870's to an Hispanic wife and had two children. This idea apparently stems from the publication of a photograph that seems

Above: The mouth of Mathews Canyon, two miles east of Elk, New Mexico on the Río Peñasco, at the approximate point where Billy Mathews built his adobe house on his homestead in 1884. *Below*: Another view of Mathews Canyon where J.B. Mathews homesteaded in 1875 and again in 1884.
Courtesy: The Author, October 1997.

to have been incorrectly identified. The photograph appeared in Lavash, *Sheriff William Brady: Tragic Hero of the Lincoln County War,* with the caption, "Jacob B. (Billy) Mathews, his wife, Candelaria and children. Late 1870's." The same picture is in John P. Wilson's 1987 book, *Merchants, Guns & Money: The Story of Lincoln County and Its Wars.* However, the man in the picture does not appear to be J.B. Mathews.

The Lincoln County marriage records show no earlier marriage. The Lincoln County Historical Society has no evidence of a previous marriage. Lillian Bidal's research has turned up no sign of an earlier marriage. Finally, the descendants of Mathews have no knowledge of any wife prior to Dora Matilda Bates. In the absence of any convincing proof of another marriage, this notion is rejected by the descendants and the author.

Bidal states that Mathews mortgaged his homestead claim on the Feliz to Thomas Catron's bank. On February 18, 1882, Mathews transferred his 640-acre Feliz claim to Catron to pay off the bank. In the meantime, Tom Tillotson had claimed and perfected the 160-acre homestead at Mathews Spring. Together with his father-in-law, James T. Bates, Mathews bought Tillotson's homestead on March 20, 1884. At last Mathews owned a piece of the claim where he and Frank Freeman had 'squatted' several years earlier. Mathews hired former sheriff George 'Dad' Peppin and Carlay Bartlett of Lincoln to build an adobe house on the homestead for him and his new wife. Other workers from La Luz also helped on the project.

In the Griffin interview, Ralph Bates said that he drove one of two wagons to Las Cruces for his brother-in-law, where Mathews bought furniture for the new house. On the way they stopped in Tularosa to buy supplies, and Mathews flashed a big roll of cash. The proprietor of the store told him to be careful. "That tough-looking customer who just went outside saw your roll. He is one of a gang of cut-throats who are hanging out at Coghlan's Well, at the point of White Sands. It will be late when you get there, but don't camp near the well—those fellows are bad."

Mathews made his plans for a probable encounter with the toughs. He cleaned his .45 pistol and greased it with butter from the chuck

The Robert N. Mullin Collection identifies this photograph as Dora Bates and Billy Mathews' wedding portrait, however, it bears little resemblance to Dora and Billy and the family believes it is of one of Dora's sisters and her husband. It was published in Frederick Nolan, *The Lincoln County War: A Documentary History* (1992).

box. He told Bates, "When we get to Coghlan's Well, if the tough eggs are there, you water both teams and I'll stay on my wagon and watch them." When they came in view of the well, Bates said, sure enough the outlaws were hanging around the corral waiting for them. "Billy slipped his gun from the holster and held it cocked under his coat, while I watered the horses," Bates stated. "Where you goin', buddy?" one of the men asked. Bates replied that they were going to Las Cruces. "What's the matter with that feller on the wagon; why don't he help you water the horses?" the desperado demanded. Bates told the man that his partner was sick and wasn't up to helping him. "If your partner is sick, you better stay the night here with us. Plenty room. Be glad to have you," the man said. Bates told him thanks but they would continue on their way. The suspicious fellow said, "Going on, eh? Well, I know that feller. Maybe he's sick and maybe he ain't." Bates and Mathews drove away and kept going until after darkness fell. They then pulled a considerable distance off the road and camped without building a fire. "The tough hombres failed to find us," Bates concluded, so the furniture-buying excursion was a success.

Dora and Billy's first child, Edith Thornton Mathews, was born June 7, 1884, at the Mathews homestead on the Lower Peñasco. She was named after William T. Thornton, a Santa Fe attorney who later became governor of the Territory. Mathews helped Thornton find investment opportunities and they became good friends; the Thorntons were guests at the Mathews' new house. When Edith was a year old, Thornton registered a brand for her and gave her sixty young heifers as a namesake gift. The Mathews herd kept growing until it numbered about eight hundred.

Bess Dow, Edith's daughter, said that as a small child Edith often spent time with the J.J. Dolan family at the Flying H Ranch. After Caroline Fritz Dolan died in 1886, Dolan hired Eva Maria Whitlock as a governess or nurse to care for his little girls, Louise and Bessie. On one occasion, according to Mathews family tradition, one of the children fell in a stream and Billy Mathews jumped in and saved her. Dolan invited little Edith Mathews to benefit from Miss Whitlock's teaching, which was the only education Edith had before the Mathews family moved to Roswell. Dolan and Miss Whitlock were married in

Left: Dora Bates Mathews and her first child, Edith, c. 1884-85. *Right*: Edith Thornton Mathews, as a young lady, c. late 1890s. By Haddix, Roswell, New Mexico.
Both photos courtesy: Jesse Bates, Elk, New Mexico.

1888 in a union that was not altogether peaceful and eventually ended in divorce. Dolan later married a woman named Mary.

While it is not the purpose here to recount the history of the CA Bar Ranch, Billy Mathews' association with it makes necessary some attention to the subject. Lillian Bidal provides much useful information about the ranch in her history of the Peñasco Valley.

The Champion Cattle Company of Texas was owned mostly by investors who lived in Missouri. The company was chartered in Texas and headquartered at Colorado City in Mitchell County. By 1883, Champion had 30,000 cattle on its West Texas range. The company used the 'CA' (CA Bar) after the initials of some of the owners (George M. Casey, William and John Adair) as one of its brands.

In the fall of 1884, Champion expanded its range into the Pecos Valley of New Mexico. It started a side operation in the Peñasco Valley, which was intended to be a negligible addition. However, it quickly grew into a large ranch known by its brand, the 'CA Bar.' Mathews, Buck Powell, and Thornton, who was an investor in the Champion Cattle Company, were behind the effort to get the big ranch to locate in the Peñasco Valley. By a series of land swaps, Powell's claim at a large spring near the east end of the valley was converted into the CA Bar headquarters. That spring has been called 'Wolz Spring,' 'Buck Powell Spring,' 'CA Bar Spring,' and 'Runyan Spring' (in 1999 the spring continued to fill the fish ponds at Runyan's trout farm). The Powell family continued to reside on their claim and Powell worked for the CA Bar as a wagon master and trail boss. The house that Powell had built for his family became the ranch headquarters in an area that included parts of sections 28 and 29 of Township 16 S., Range 17 E.

Billy Mathews took on the job of postmaster of the new Lower Peñasco post office on November 11, 1884. Sources are not clear, but apparently the post office was at the CA Bar headquarters in an adobe building that had two fireplaces and rifle portholes for defense. The headquarters was situated about seven miles southeast (down

Above: CA Bar Ranch House, 1896. Built by J.F. Hinkle in 1896, it is now the Runyan Trout Farm. Photo # 057L.
Below: CA Bar cowboys and chuck wagon, Peñasco Cattle Company, March 1897. Photo # 2082.
Both photos courtesy: Historical Center for Southeast New Mexico, Roswell.

Above: This adobe house is believed to have been the Mathews family house when he was resident manager of the CA Bar Ranch, west of Hope, New Mexico, on the Río Peñasco.
Below: Lower Peñasco Post Office where J.B. Mathews was the first postmaster in 1884. Both buildings are now on the Runyan Ranch & Trout Farm.
                    Courtesy: The Author, October 1997.

stream) from Mathews' home, and the old post office building was still in use in 1999 as a barn on the Runyan ranch.

Life must have been good for the young, newly-wed rancher. Lincoln's newspaper, the *Golden Era*, reported on December 4, 1884: "Buck Powell, W.C. Warren, and Billy Mathews, about the liveliest spike team that ever comes to town, pulled in from the Peñasco a few days ago to rig out in dude clothes and buy calico and Christmas presents ...."

Mathews' tenure as postmaster was short-lived. When he became involved with the CA Bar Ranch, he turned the postmaster's job over to his wife. Dora Mathews, who served from January 21, 1885, until April 26, 1886, was the youngest postmistress in the Territory. Documentary evidence is lacking, but the tradition handed down from one valley generation to the next is that Billy, Dora, and baby Edith Mathews moved to the CA Bar headquarters soon after the post office opened and may have lived for a time in the post office building. What happened to their own adobe at Mathews Spring is unknown; no trace of its exact location has been found in modern times.

The wide-spread drought of 1885 caused conditions to deteriorate on Champion's Texas range, so the company chose to relocate a considerable part of its livestock to the Peñasco. The company hired Billy Mathews with the title of "assistant resident manager." According to Lillian Bidal in an interview with the present writer, there was a resident manager, but he is never identified in any of the records. Mathews' first big job was to trail-boss the cattle drive to the Peñasco from Texas. He and his drovers trailed the herd of eight hundred beeves across the plains following along the tracks of the Texas & Pacific Railroad. The herd arrived on the Peñasco in October 1885. Another herd was shipped to Toyah, Texas, and then driven to the ranch. The CA Bar herd was further increased by another eight hundred when Mathews used his cattle to buy an interest in the company.

Twenty-three-year-old James F. Hinkle was one of the cow punchers who arrived with the herd. His uncle, John H. Hinkle, was a principal investor in the Champion Cattle Co.; and his father, Miles P.

James F. Hinkle, the 'Cowboy Governor,' shown here at the Cowboy Reunion, Las Vegas, New Mexico, 1923, came to the CA Bar in 1885 as a drover, became resident manager in 1892, and later president of the company. He was elected governor of New Mexico in 1922.
Courtesy: Historical Center for Southeast New Mexico, Roswell, Photo # 2317D.

Hinkle, was also an investor in the company. 'Jimmy,' as Hinkle was called by his friends, was destined to be Mathews' successor as manager of the CA Bar, a member of the Territorial Legislature, a future governor of New Mexico (1923-24), and a prominent Roswell banker.

At first, the CA Bar could not show a profit. The company treasurer, Harvey W. Salmon, asked college-educated Jimmy Hinkle to look at the company's books. His expertise helped the ranching venture become more cost-effective. The company shortly appointed Hinkle as bookkeeper, and he continued with that duty until 1892. Hinkle also succeeded Dora Mathews as postmaster of Lower Peñasco in 1886, with the post office in his bedroom at the ranch headquarters. Whether or not both Hinkle and the Mathews family lived in the former Powell house is unknown. The Mathews family may have lived in another adobe house nearby (which was still in use in 1998). Later, Hinkle's responsibilities expanded considerably when he was named foreman of the ranch.

In 1886, Billy Mathews was promoted to resident manager of the CA Bar. The cattle company continuously enlarged its land holdings, mostly by rewarding workers if they would file homestead claims and then swap them for stock in the company–a practice that was contrary to the spirit, if not the letter, of the homestead law. In some cases farmers were paid to make such claims, according to Bidal. As was customary at the time, the ranch used the open range which surrounded the watering places which they owned. Several times a year, roundups separated the cattle that belonged to the various ranches and which all roamed more-or-less together on the open range.

Mathews and James Bates' joint property at Mathews Spring was incorporated into the CA Bar company on January 22, 1887. After this deal was made, the James Bates family left the Peñasco Valley and relocated to Wooten.

Acquisition of the Mathews Spring property gave the CA Bar the water rights to the two largest springs on the river. One of the problems with irrigating from the Peñasco was that there was a gap of some twelve miles–the 'Middle Peñasco'–between the flowing water of the Upper Peñasco and the springs at the head of the Lower Peñasco.

The water disappeared into sinkholes, and that segment of the river did not flow except from rainfall. According to an affidavit reproduced in Bidal's Peñasco Valley book, J.J. Dolan testified in a water-rights case that Mathews, Powell, and others acting in behalf of Champion Cattle Company built a ditch in 1885 that reached from the sinks on the Upper Peñasco downstream for some thirty miles. The amount of water at their disposal for irrigation increased considerably. A well-known part of the lore of the valley is how the men drove cattle through the ditch to pack the ground. When the drought that had resulted in the CA Bar's move to the Peñasco in the first place ended in 1888, the Champion Cattle Company expanded into Arizona Territory by buying the Coronado Cattle Company in eastern Arizona on the Gila River.

Among those who filed claims on the Peñasco for the CA Bar company was Robert 'Bob' Mathews, J.B.'s younger brother. Bob Mathews hired on as a cowboy at the ranch after he came west from Tennessee on his doctor's orders, seeking a drier climate for his health. One of his assignments was to travel to El Paso in the spring of 1888 to meet the train and accompany Hennig Von Bosse back to the ranch.

The young German became a cowboy on the CA Bar; in his old age, he wrote about the experience. When he first saw Bob Mathews in El Paso, Hennig described him as "... a lean, young fellow with a still leaner face that bespoke of lung trouble and a sharp pointed nose at the end of which a little drop of moisture seemed about to take a fall. Bud (Bernard Cleve, Von Bosse's cousin) introduced him to me as Bob, a brother of the ranch boss." Von Bosse's memoirs relate how the two of them had many adventures on the long ride back to the Peñasco and, later, as co-workers on the ranch.

Lillian Bidal states in a letter to the author that Homestead Application records in the New Mexico State Records Center and Archives reveal that Robert Mathews filed two claims near Hope. These claims were caught up in litigation by the Champion Cattle Company, and Mathews' final patents were denied.

Two other children were born to Billy and Dora Mathews while they lived on the CA Bar: Ernest Houston Mathews in 1886 and Cora

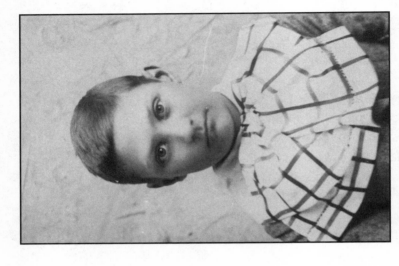

Left: Cora Lea Mathews, youngest child of Dora and Billy Mathews, c. 1890s.
Right: Ernest Houston Mathews, only son of Dora and Billy Mathews, c. .1890.
Both photos courtesy: Jesse Bates, Elk, New Mexico.

The J.B. 'Billy' Mathews family, c. 1890. *l-r*: son Ernest; wife Dora; unidentified man (may be Ben Wayland who later married Dora's sister Eolin Bates); Maude Bates, Dora's sister; daughter Edith. Seated man, holding baby Cora, is said to be Mathews. Some family members believe the seated man does not appear to be Mathews, but is Ralph Bates, Mrs. Mathews' brother, or the husband of one of Dora's sisters.

Courtesy: Jesse Bates, Elk, New Mexico.

Lea Mathews in 1888. Their lives on the ranch could be quite exciting. On one occasion some Mescalero Apaches came by unexpectedly. Dora Mathews was washing clothes outdoors when an Apache woman came into the yard and 'borrowed' a hatchet (or axe, or washpot, according to other versions of the story). Dora quickly picked up her gun and recovered the stolen property posthaste.

J.B. Mathews took a very active part in the life of the Valley community, most often in the interest of the CA Bar Ranch. In an effort to control overcrowding of the ranges with cattle and sheep, local ranchers formed the District Protective Association of Precinct 9 in 1884. They appointed Mathews to a committee to write a constitution for the group. Another example is the Guadalupe Valley Reservoir, Irrigating, and Manufacturing Company (GVRI&M), which organized for the fourth time in 1890. Apparently this 'paper' company did not succeed in accomplishing very many of its goals. According to Bidal, it was a "tenuous coalition of approximately sixty farmers and ranchers ..." who proposed to "... construct and maintain ditches, canals, reservoirs and pipelines to hold and conduct water for irrigation of land for agricultural purposes, the cultivating, buying and selling farm or other products ... ." Documents in the papers of Governor James F. Hinkle, Rio Grande Historical Collections, New Mexico State University, show that Mathews was first elected treasurer; then on April 7, 1891, he was appointed general manager. Hinkle was president, W.W. Paul was vice-president, and T.C. Tillotson was secretary-treasurer.

The GVRI&M Company soon reorganized again, on August 21, 1891–this time as The Peñasco Reservoir and Irrigation Company. The ambitious organizers elected A.B. Fall as president at a proposed annual salary of $40,000; James F. Hinkle as secretary-treasurer at a salary of $25,000; Peter Corn as vice-president at $10,000; and J.B. Mathews as general manager at $20,000. In the process of re-organizing the company, all stockholders' shares were re-issued and discounted 20%. Mathews had 55 shares valued at $27,500 in the Guadalupe Company; after re-issue, they equalled 220 shares worth $22,000. This company and a number of similar organizations were soon caught up in a maze of litigation over water rights on the Peñasco that lasted for many years.

*   *   *

The Lower Peñasco area, in which the principal activities of the CA Bar Ranch were located, remained in Lincoln County for a time even after Chaves County and Eddy County were organized in 1891. This continued until 1899, the year that Otero County was organized. If the Lower Peñasco were to become a part of Otero County, those who lived there faced laborious trips over the mountains to Alamogordo to reach the new county seat. Roswell was more convenient and was also the trading center for the area. Through the efforts of James F. Hinkle and other residents of the valley, the Lower Peñasco became a part of the 'bootheel' portion of Chaves County while the Middle and Upper portions of the Valley went into the new county.

In February 1891, the shareholders of the CA Bar Ranch created a New Mexico corporation called The Peñasco Cattle Company, which was separate from the Champion Cattle Company of Texas. Directors of the new corporation were George M. Casey of Missouri, who was the company president; Casey's son, Thomas; and Mathews, Hinkle, and Thornton. Mathews was 'promoted' to vice-president, which effectively relieved him of the responsibility of the day-to-day operation of the ranch. However, as an officer and stockholder in the company, he was still very much interested in the operations of the ranch. He transferred various parcels of land in which he had an interest to the company, presumably in exchange for shares, on March 2, 1891; February 18, 1892; and April 20, 1893. James F. Hinkle was promoted to the position of resident ranch manager, a position he held for the entire life of the corporation. He later became president of the company.

The only known surviving document in J.B. Mathews' own hand is a letter which he wrote to James F. Hinkle in 1891 and is in the Hinkle papers. The letter provides an interesting look at the man as well as the times:

Left: CA Bar cowboy quarters built by homesteader Buck Powell. This first HQ of CA Bar Ranch may have been the Mathews family residence. Photo 057G. *Right:* Another view of the Powell homestead. Photo 057A.

Both photos courtesy: Historical Center for Southeast New Mexico, Roswell.

Lincoln N M
December 26th 1891

J.F. Hinkle Esq
    Clinton Mo
My Dear Jimmy=
          I arrived here on 24th inst. Found the road very bad between Hondo and Felix. Yesterday was the coldest day I ever saw in this town. The thermometer stood at 17 below zero all day, with a cold wind, so we did not get out much and it is still cold but no wind. Lincoln is very quiet. They had a dance on Christmas Eve but we did not attend as I was unwell. Hope you had a nice time Christmas. Mrs. McGiness has taken charge of the Press here and will run the paper. So you see we will have a paper in the county sits. The weather is so cold I don't think I shall go to Roswell for the installation on the 28th. Your Girl looks as sweet as ever and is going to Penasco soon. Write me all the news. Write me here. I will be here for some time yet but will be on hand at Eddy. Thornton has gone to Chas. Wingfield's for Christmas. Wishing you a happy New Year I am as ever
                    Yours Truly etc
                    J.B. Mathews

Mathews' reference to the newspaper in Lincoln was the *Independent*; and the term "county sits" may be an attempt at humor. The "installation on the 28th" no doubt refers to the Masonic lodge in Roswell. "Your Girl" is a reference to Lillie Roberts, who lived in Lincoln with her uncle, Lincoln County Sheriff Daniel Roberts; Hinkle and Miss Lillie were married on December 14, 1892, just before he began serving his first term in the Territorial Legislature. Mathews' allusion to Eddy was probably a meeting of the directors of one of the corporations in which he and Hinkle were involved.

The Buck Powell/CA Bar Spring now feeds the trout ponds at Runyan Trout Farm.
Courtesy: The Author, October 1997.

V

BACK TO THE PECOS VALLEY

The Mathews family moved into Roswell in January 1893 so the children might have access to a school. On December 29, 1892, Dora had arranged to purchase a lot at 201 N. Pennsylvania Avenue, on the northeast corner of the intersection with West Second Street, and they proceeded with plans to build a residence for the family. In addition, they bought half interest in a one-inch water well on the North Spring River several blocks north of their home. Later, they secured a license for an artesian well on their home lot.

His income as a director of the CA Bar Ranch, Mathews believed, would be enough for his family's primary source of support. Forces beyond his control, however, interfered with those plans: drouths, floods, a drastic decline in the market for cattle, and the depression known as the 'Panic of 1893.' Mathews continued to have an active interest in the ranch, but he needed another way to earn his livelihood.

According to Frederick Nolan in *The Lincoln County War: A Documentary History*, Mathews "was bankrupted" because he served as bondsman for Frank Lesnet, the receiver in the new Federal Land Office in Roswell. Lesnet disappeared in early 1893 with his accounts short by $8,900.00. Nolan claims that Mathews was left holding the bag; however, the records do not list Mathews as one of Lesnet's bondsmen. Ernest Mathews said that it was Sheriff Charles C. Perry for whom his father served as bondsman, which was a few years later.

*   *   *

Soon after Mathews moved his family to Roswell, J.J. Hagerman's Pecos Irrigation & Improvement Company, according to both Nolan and Fulton, engaged him as manager of the company. Other sources indicate that the position was as manager of only the company's South Spring Ranch, which is likely correct. The company had a farm and orchard at John S. Chisum's former ranch headquarters. Whether Mathews had the position at South Spring already lined up before he left the CA Bar is not clear, but he moved his family to the Chisum place sometime in 1893 and lived there until 1896. According to Ernest, Edith stayed in town with Amelia and J.P. Church while school was in session; and Ernest rode his horse to school from the ranch for three years, 1894-96.

J.B. Mathews planted five hundred acres in alfalfa on the Chisum farm and also experimented with sugar beets. A change in Hagerman's corporate structure soon placed Mathews under a subsidiary of the Pecos Irrigation & Improvement Company. The new company was called Roswell Land & Water Company, which was incorporated on June 21, 1894, for a period of twenty years.

Ernest Mathews describes how his mother had a large flock of turkeys at the Chisum Ranch when crews were building the Pecos Valley Railway into Roswell from Eddy (Carlsbad) in 1894. The laborers carried off her turkeys when they left. Since the workers were going to Mexico, where the tariff on the horses was greater than their value, the men gave their seven horses to Ernest. Ernest writes that he and his father rode the first train into Roswell from South Spring in October 1894.

J.B. Mathews resigned from his position at the South Spring Ranch in October 1896, presumably because of continuing hard times for J.J. Hagerman's financial empire. The Mathews family moved into their house in Roswell, and J.B. began to consider what he might do next to support his family. He had been politically active in earlier years. When Mathews was still running the CA Bar, he and Tom

Tillotson served as delegates to the Lincoln County Republican convention in 1886.

According to Ernest, his father served as a bondsman for Sheriff Charles C. Perry, who took off for parts unknown in June 1896 with $7,639 in Chaves County tax revenues. Mathews was not one of the original bondsmen for Perry, but one who was—W.H. Guyse—died; and the county commissioners requested that the judge order Perry to renew his bond. However, the official records do not show that this was ever done, so there is no evidence that Mathews was Perry's surety.

Whether Sheriff Perry's shenanigans influenced Mathews to seek that office the same year is not known; but he did decide at the last minute to run for sheriff in the general election of 1896. There were rumors that J.J. Hagerman was behind it because he wanted to promote Republican influence in the political affairs of Democratic Chaves County. Hagerman wrote to company officials in Eddy from his home in Colorado Springs to assure them that there was no truth to this allegation, and the local newspapers ran the letter.

Actually, Mathews ran on an Independent ticket because he wanted to attract Democratic as well as Republican votes. Besides, he announced too late to receive the endorsement of the local Republican Party. Mathews' official announcement appeared in the October 30, 1896, edition of the *Roswell Record*:

TO THE VOTERS OF CHAVES COUNTY, N.M.
Upon the earnest solicitation of my friends, both in the Democratic and Republican parties, I have, this day, tendered my resignation to the R.L. & W. Co. [Roswell Land & Water Co.], as foreman of the Chisum Ranch, and herewith announce that I will stand for election on an Independent Ticket, for the office of Sheriff of Chaves county. If elected, I hereby pledge my best personal endeavors to the rigid enforcement of the criminal laws, and also for a careful and economical administration of the duties of this office; and respectfully solicit the support of all citizens, irrespective of party, who are interested in the cause of good local government.

J.B. (Billy,) MATHEWS.

If, as the announcement states, Mathews resigned his job "on this date," that would have been October 30, the date of the newspaper. The election was just a few days later, so he had almost no time to mount an official campaign. Although he ran as an independent, everyone knew he was a Republican. Bess Dow said her grandmother, Dora, who was a faithful Democrat, was quite chagrinned by her husband's Republican politics. She was very relieved when Mathews lost the election to the incumbent, C.W. Haynes, by 339 votes to 193. Haynes had been appointed sheriff by the governor only months before the election, after Sheriff Perry fled with county tax revenues.

In the next weekly issue of the *Record*, the editor chided Mathews a bit by commenting, "Billy Mathews still 'smiles' just as though nothing had happened. Billy says he is now convinced that he is a political failure." In the heavily partisan tradition of newspapers of the times, the Democratic *Roswell Record* wasted no space reporting on the 1896 election results—it being a foregone conclusion that the Democratic ticket would win, hands down. Considering that Mathews received 36% of the votes, he did rather well for such a short campaign.

Mathews never shied away from active involvement in civic, community, and fraternal affairs. This was despite the fact that he was a Republican and a Union veteran in a town that was dominated by Democrats and Confederate veterans, such as Captain Joseph C. Lea, the 'Father of Roswell,' and Lea's old Civil War comrade, Captain Jason W. James. There is no indication that Mathews ever tried to pass himself off as a Confederate veteran in order to enhance his political and financial interests. Further, there is no evidence that the fallacious view that Mathews was a Confederate veteran arose while he was still living. On the other hand, there is much evidence that Mathews was accepted throughout Southeast New Mexico as one of the 'good old boys.'

The house that the Mathews family had constructed while they lived at the Chisum Ranch was a four-bedroom residence built on their property at 201 N. Pennsylvania. They moved into it in 1896 when he resigned from the Roswell Land & Water Co. The *Roswell*

Register for February 27, 1897, notes, "Billy Mathews is putting new porches on his Second St. residence, and will soon have one of the snuggest little homes in town." James Hinkle also built a house two lots north of the Mathews home in 1897-98 so his family would have a place to stay when they came in from the CA Bar Ranch. In December 1900, the Mathews family bought the house and lot next door to their home.

Mathews' activities from 1896 to 1898 are obscure for the most part. He apparently had a number of investments in land and city lots; the deed records for Chaves County show a total of twenty transactions involving Mathews between 1882 and 1903. However, it seems clear that his main energies concerned his interest and office in the Peñasco Cattle Co. The Roswell newspapers during those years make frequent mentions of his comings-and-goings between Roswell and the CA Bar Ranch, the Feliz Ranch of J.J. Dolan, Lincoln, Las Cruces, and Arizona as he attended to cattle business and the work of the corporation.

In later years, Edith told stories to her daughter, Bess Maddux Dow, about how it was to grow up in Roswell in the 1890s. At one time, there was a tent in the Mathews' back yard where Joseph Dixon, a former slave which the family referred to as 'Old Black Joe,' resided while he worked for the family. Dixon was quite well known. The people of Roswell held him in high esteem, but they called him 'Laughing Joe' because he suffered from a nervous disorder (Tourette's syndrome) that caused him to laugh at inappropriate times. Edith fondly remembered that Dixon danced—another symptom of Tourette's—while he washed the family's dishes. Dixon's employment by the Mathews family is confirmed by other sources.

Another story that Mrs. Dow related was about an interesting incident that happened when Edith was a small child. At some point after they moved to Roswell, Billy and Dora Mathews affiliated themselves with the First Christian Church (although their descendant, Joanne McCombs, said that Mathews' denominational background was Episcopalian). As was the common practice of several Roswell churches in those days, the converts were baptized by immersion in the North Spring River. Little Edith just knew her parents were about to drown, so she vowed never to be baptized herself!

Mathews became a 32nd Degree Scottish Rite Mason while residing in Elizabethtown in the late 1860's. When the Roswell Masons were raising funds in the fall of 1888 to build their first temple, Mathews pledged $100, as did many other prominent men in the county. On May 23, 1891, he was elected to membership in Roswell Lodge No. 18, Ancient Free & Accepted Masons. After a disastrous fire in January 1893 destroyed the Masonic Temple on Main Street, he contributed another $100 to the fund to put up a new building. Mathews served as Senior Steward in 1894 and as Junior Deacon in 1895. When the Rio Hondo Commandery No. 6, Knights Templar, installed new officers in December 1897, Mathews was included as standard-bearer.

According to Bidal, Mathews began a "desperate" search for employment in the late 1890's; and some of his influential Missouri friends connected with the CA Bar Ranch helped him secure a federal job. Some evidence suggests that Mathews campaigned for an appointment as postmaster of Roswell when Lucius K. McGaffey's term was approaching expiration. McGaffey's appointment was supposed to end on April 10, 1898, according to the *Roswell Record*, but "... President McKinley's time is too much occupied to be making appointments just now"—because of the tensions with Spain over Cuba.

Two items in the *Roswell Record*, the first on April 15, 1898, and the other a week later, indicate Mathews' interest:

> Billy Mathews struck out on the railroad Tuesday (he went on the train). In answer to inquiries as to his destination he said he was taking advantage of the five days armistice to go to Washington and demand the post office. That was one of Billy's jokes. The editor met him on the road and knows that he is gone to Las Cruces to preside at the annual meeting of the directors of the Penasco Cattle Co.

Billy Mathews has returned. He says that he did not go to Washington, as his transportation did not read that way, and besides, when he came to think about it, he was afraid that the armistice would be off and the President be too busy to talk to him.

The 'armistice' to which the newspaper refers was the time when the president was preparing to ask Congress to declare war on Spain, but he delayed it in order to give Spain a chance to submit to American demands.

President William McKinley appointed Mathews to the position of postmaster of Roswell on May 19, 1898, effective July 1, succeeding McGaffey in the position. There is no question that the appointment was a political issue. R.S. Hamilton, editor of the *Roswell Register*, claimed no political stance but tended to lean toward Republican causes. His May 13 announcement of Mathews' appointment was deemed worthy of a front-page item, along with an engraving of Mathews' portrait; rarely did the Roswell papers put local news on the front page in those days. In the article, the editor gave a short biography of the appointee and concluded, "Mr. Mathews has been a staunch Republican all his life. He is a prominent member of all the Masonic orders in Roswell and commands the respect and esteem of all who know him."

On the other hand, the editor of the *Roswell Record* made no bones about the Democratic stand of his paper. In the May 13, 1898, issue, Lucius Dills took this opportunity to blast the Republican administration in his page three article:

BILLY GETS THE POSTOFFICE

When the news came last Friday evening that President McKinley had sent the name of J.B. Mathews to the Senate for confirmation as postmaster for Roswell, our people breathed freely once more. Former appointments made by the President for this section have not been of the kind to inspire our people with the belief that the President cared much for the wishes of our people, and as he had a chance to repeat the former doses, in making a selection for postoffice, our people were naturally on the anxious seat until the appointment was made.

The Masonic Temple, 1900, was at the corner of Third and
Main Streets in Roswell. The post office door was at the back,
facing Third Street. The Masons used the second floor; the
Roswell Book Store was on the first floor fronting Main Street.
This was the location of the post office when J.B. Mathews was
postmaster, 1898-1904.
Courtesy: Historical Center for Southeast New Mexico, Roswell, Photo # 2250A.

Several other good men in Roswell were applicants for the place and the appointment of either would not have been distasteful to the patrons of the office; but there were others. In appointing Billy Mathews for the place, President McKinley has given our people a man who is both efficient and popular. We feel that the President deserves a vote of thanks from our people in this matter. Billy will, beyond question, be confirmed and will probably take hold about the first of June. He will enter upon his duties with the good wishes of almost the entire community, including those of every one of the other applicants for the place, who would have been in any degree satisfactory to the people.

Before Mathews could embark upon his new career as postmaster, he had to conclude some of his cattle operations. These activities were reported in the June 10 and June 17 issues of the *Roswell Record:*

Billy Mathews came home Monday and left again Tuesday to finish up the shipment of the CA— cattle upon which he has been engaged for the past month. He expects to return by the middle of next week and will then go into the post office and take lessons under Postmaster McGaffey before taking charge himself.

Billy Mathews has finished up his cattle business at El Paso and is now irregular assistant to Postmaster McGaffey. Billy says he is learning the business so that he can take hold at the end of the quarter.

Mathews assumed the postmaster's position on July 1, 1898. Several important milestones were achieved by the Roswell Post Office while Mathews was postmaster, according to Jim White, Farmington Postmaster and New Mexico postal historian. A major change in the handling of mail took place in 1899 when the Pecos Valley & Northeastern Railway was completed between Roswell and Amarillo, Texas. The new extension provided a much more efficient connection with points east and north than did the previous route.

The Roswell Post Office made history in 1902 when Postmaster Mathews presided over the establishment of the first rural mail route in the Territory. Started on January 1, the twenty-eight-mile-long route served 120 families in the closely-settled agricultural area north and east of town. The mail carrier was Walter Gill, son and successor of the founder of Roswell Seed Company, John Gill. For more than a year, this was the only rural mail route in New Mexico.

Another sign of postal progress took place in 1902 under Mathews' purview. As the result of increased revenues in the office, Roswell was advanced from a third-class to a second-class post office on July 1, 1902.

An amusing story about Billy Mathews as postmaster appeared in the *Roswell Record* in September 1901 when the paper chided him somewhat because he forgot to close the post office on Labor Day: "The Roswell post office has been in deep mourning this week. Postmaster Mathews forgot that Monday was labor day and a legal holiday and the office was kept open as usual."

In 1902, President Theodore Roosevelt re-appointed Mathews, and he held the job until his death in 1904. Edith, his daughter, worked there under him, starting as a money-order clerk. When Mathews made his frequent trips out of town on Masonic business, Dora and Edith ran the postoffice for him. Edith's own daughter, Bess Dow, also maintained the family tradition by working at the Roswell Post Office.

Although Billy Mathews was no longer involved in the direct operation of the CA Bar Ranch, he remained an officer and a stockholder. In *Pisacah: A Place of Plenty*, Lillian Bidal provides a narrative of the demise of the cattle empire that was essentially controlled by the Casey and Salmon families of Missouri. They had ranching operations in six states and territories. Many factors contributed to the downfall of their empire, but the main problem seemed to be conflict with encroaching farmers over water rights and land titles.

Between 1897 and 1899, the Peñasco Cattle Company borrowed from various creditors in Missouri and Texas until their debt reached $177,073.34. All of the loans were bought up by Strahorn-Hutton-Evans Commission Company of Missouri. Casey and Salmon sold land to pay the interest on their notes, so the CA Bar died a slow death over a period of years. Hinkle finally began closing it out in 1901.

Ralph Bates, Dora Bates Mathews' brother, in his 1937 interview with Fred Griffin, related how he owned stock in the CA Bar and felt that his future was secure. "Our future looked rosy until the panic of the early nineties put a crimp in the cow business." Jesse Bates of the Peñasco Valley, a grandson of Ralph, told Lillian Bidal that his grandfather and other farmers were bitter because they had lost so much when the CA Bar folded. He said most of the settlers who had invested their property and/or livestock in the corporation were bankrupted, losing everything they had or might have. Until the mid-1930's, Jesse stated, Ralph Bates put all property in his wife's name because of the bankruptcy.

Billy Mathews was caught in a desperate situation by the collapse of the CA Bar because his name was on one of the notes held by Strahorn-Hutton-Evans. The amount of the note has not been learned; but whatever it was, Mathews couldn't pay it. A letter to 'Jimmie' Hinkle in the Hinkle papers, Rio Grande Historical Collections, New Mexico State University, from George Casey and dated March 14, 1902, indicates that both Mathews and Hinkle had written to Casey to ask him to pay or help Mathews pay the note. Casey replied that he didn't have the money or the collateral to pay it. He suggested that Mathews borrow on his Roswell city lots and offer to pay out the remainder from his salary as postmaster. In another letter from Casey to Hinkle, dated March 29, 1902, his tone seems to be a bit more urgent:

> ... Now, Jim, I wish you would talk to Billy about what he owes [Col.] Simpson [of Strahorn-Hutton-Evans]. Will he or has he allready bin reappointed Post master. How is his property. I am not on the note. I have a letter from Simpson that he is going to bring suit. Billy does not say anything to him. Do all you can to help Billy and so will I ... .

Still another letter on the same subject is definitely more blunt about Mathews' debt. On April 29, 1902, Casey wrote to Hinkle:

My Dear Jimmie:-

Your letter of the 23rd just received. I thank you very much for your trouble with Billy. I cannot do as you suggest. He must pay it, or a part of it, and then I will do as much for him as any of his friends there will do. It is not right for you or him to ask me to pay this debt, and carry him for the money. It does not suit me, and I cannot do it ....

No records exist to indicate what Mathews' disposition of this matter was, but when he died about two years later this debt was not listed among his obligations and he seemed to have plenty of money.

The Missouri investors in the CA Bar and other cattle operations also went under, according to Bidal. George Casey was in poor health so he turned his financial matters over to his son, Thomas. Thomas Casey, a lawyer by profession, became the cashier and later the manager of the Salmon and Salmon Bank, which belonged to his father-in-law. When the younger Casey saw the family fortune going down the drain, he could not bear to see his father's good name tainted. He altered the bank books and got caught. Missouri bank examiners closed the bank in June 1905, and Casey was sent to prison for five years to pay for his misdeeds.

J.B. 'Billy' Mathews near the end of his life, c. 1900.
By A.M. Parker, Roswell, New Mexico.
Courtesy: The Robert N. Mullin Collection,
Nita Stewart Haley Memorial Library, Midland, Texas. Photo #154.

VI

CONCLUSION

Mathews attended a Masonic function in Santa Fe in May 1904, and was stricken with pneumonia while there. He returned home to Roswell and fought the illness for about three weeks. At one point, he rallied but suffered a relapse and went into a coma for several days. Death was expected for about twenty-four hours before it finally came. On June 3, 1904, the old pioneer died at the age of fifty-seven. He was survived by his widow, Dora, and their three children. Ernest and Cora still lived with their mother at the family home, although Ernest worked as a cowboy at the Diamond A Ranch most of the time. Edith had married. Her husband, Robert Maddux, was the Roswell city marshal.

Elder C.C. Hill of the First Christian Church conducted the short funeral service at the Mathews home, 201 N. Pennsylvania, at 2:30 p.m. on June 5, 1904. The Masonic officers then took over and, with a Knights Templar escort, buried him in the Masonic Circle of Southside Cemetery. All the casket-bearers were leading men of Roswell: William M. Atkinson, Edward A. Cahoon, Nathan Jaffa, Smith Lea, John W. Poe, and John T. Stone.

The *Roswell Daily Record* was lavish in its praise of Mathews:

'Billy Mathews' as he was familiarly known, was one of the few men whom everybody liked. In his nature there was a geniality that made everybody his friend. The stranger, who would meet him but for a few minutes conversation, would walk away from him feeling that he had known him for years, and for years to come he would remember him as a friend. The humor and good nature of the man was contagious. Brave to the point of daring, charitable in acts and deeds to the utmost, of broad nature and broader sympathies, it is no wonder that last evening when the report spread over town that 'Billy Mathews is dead' that every heart was heavy, and there was a lump in the throat that wouldn't down. Not because he had been a popular official, not because he had been a brave soldier in war, and a man who in the early days of the Territory had been a terror to the evil doers, but he was honored and respected for his own innate qualities of manhood that won everybody to him ... . No more popular man has ever lived or died in Chaves County than J. B. Mathews.

Mathews had not written a will, so the Chaves County Probate Judge appointed his widow, Dora, as administratrix of his estate. There were debts totalling about $2,700.00, which she paid off immediately. Probate records give no indication of bank accounts or insurance policies, but Mathews obviously had some liquid assets. Dora inherited their two lots and houses and all the furnishings in their residence. Some indication of the family's lifestyle is suggested by items on the inventory of furnishings: they owned a piano and a library of fifty books.

One of Mathews' last projects was major repair and remodeling of his house and probably the house next door that he owned. Receipts in his probate records indicate that the project was underway before his death, and it was completed by his widow during the year after he died.

Following her husband's death, Dora took in boarders to provide some income. At an undetermined time, she began to draw a pension as the widow of a Union soldier.

The Mathews family all left Roswell within a few years after J.B.'s death, some of them never to return. Edith and her family moved to Texico, New Mexico; they eventually returned to Roswell. Ernest worked at the Diamond A until about 1910. He "went broke in the

Left: Ernest Mathews, only son of J.B. and Dora, in his later years, c. 1960s.
Right: Dora Matilda Bates Mathews, c. 1915?. By Splane, Los Angeles, California.
Both photos courtesy: Jesse Bates, Elk, New Mexico.

cattle business in the Carrizozo, New Mexico country in the 1920's."
He and his wife, Marguerite Calfee Mathews, moved to California in
1926. Cora married Aubrey Smith on July 27, 1906, and moved to
Arizona. She later married a man named Honstedt and lived in Las
Vegas, Nevada, and California.

When the Old Settlers' Society of Chaves County met for the first
time in September 1905, Dora was a special honoree, according to
Bidal. In 1912, Dora married one of her boarders, Louis Moren of
California. While dates and many specifics are not available, family
tradition indicates that they moved to Helena, Montana. According
to her great-grandson, Dick Armstrong, Moren died after depleting
Dora's resources. Whether or not her marriage to Moren affected her
pension is unknown. She then supported herself by employing her
considerable skills as a seamstress; unfortunately, most of her work
was for the 'red light' district, Armstrong stated. She later moved to
California where she resided with her daughter, Cora, and cared for
the elderly as a source of income.

Sometime in 1946, officials of the Roswell Museum asked Dora
to operate the museum, Mrs. McCombs said. After a thirty-four-year
absence, she moved back to Roswell. However, at age seventy-nine,
she was unable to meet the physical challenge of the museum position. She resided at 920 East Second Street in Roswell until her death
there on October 11, 1952, at the age of eighty-five, according to the
Roswell Daily Record. Services were conducted at the Church of
Christ Scientist by Mrs. Helen Leopard. Dora was buried beside her
husband at South Park Cemetery.

J.B. Mathews lived a life filled with adventure and variety. An
interesting and unique man, he was held in high esteem by all his
friends and acquaintances. He had been a rebellious teenager who ran
away to join the Union Army while his family and neighbors were
mostly Confederates. An adventurous young man, he had built a 'nest
egg' by staking a claim in the New Mexico gold rush. He was a pioneer farmer and cattle-raiser in the Pecos Valley of Southeast New
Mexico. He served as a deputy sheriff during the turmoil of the Lincoln County War. Through his association with the CA Bar Ranch, he

A group of old-timers honored by New Mexico Military Institute, Roswell, in January 1953. *Seated, l-r*: Ella Lea Bedell Dow, Edith Mathews Maddux, Eva Hedgecoxe Barlow, Jenny James McClenny; *standing l-r*: Jennie Lea Ashinhurst, Tommie Yeary Rose, Laura Hedgecoxe Cahoon.
Courtesy: Historical Center for Southeast New Mexico, Roswell, photo # 3394C.

played a major role in the development of the cattle business. He was postmaster at Roswell for the last six years of his life. Finally, he was a family man who raised three children to become successful adults. His proud descendants have followed his examples in ranching, farming, fraternal life, and politics, as well as in education and other fields.

Pioneers like Jacob Basil 'Billy' Mathews risked much to develop their communities and build a workable society where families could live their lives in harmony and security. This book is a brief effort to recognize the accomplishments of J.B. Mathews and correct previously published misinformation.

Mathews Street in south Roswell is more than just a street. Its name should remind present-day New Mexicans that, once upon a time, Billy Mathews and many others walked before us to prepare the way for the blessings that we enjoy today.

Gravestone of J.B. and Dora Mathews, South Park Cemetery, Roswell, New Mexico.
Courtesy: The Author, August 1997.

SOURCES CONSULTED

Primary Sources

Armstrong, Richard R. 'Dick.' Personal interview by Elvis E. Fleming, October 7, 1997. Audio-tape recording, Archives, Historical Center for Southeast New Mexico, Roswell.

Armstrong, Richard R. 'Dick.' "Summary of Mathews Family History." MS, Archives, Historical Center for Southeast New Mexico, Roswell.

Bates, Jesse. Personal interviews by Elvis E. Fleming, May 22, 1996; October 23, 1997.

Bidal, Lillian. Letters to Elvis E. Fleming, April 10, 1996; June 2, 1996; July 23, 1997.

Chaves County Commissioners' Proceedings, Book A, Chaves County Courthouse, Roswell, N. M.

Chaves County Deed Records, Chaves County Courthouse, Roswell, N. M.

Chaves County Probate Records, No. 110 (J. B. Mathews). Chaves County Courthouse, Roswell, N. M.

Chaves County Record of Official Bonds, Book A, Chaves County Courthouse, Roswell, N. M.

Dow, Bess. Personal interview by Elvis E. Fleming, February 26, 1 9 8 3 . Audio-tape Recording, Archives, Historical Center for Southeast New Mexico, Roswell.

Dow, Bess. "Mathews and Maddux Families." Paper presented to the Chaves County Historical Society, March 14, 1983. MS, Archives, Historical Center for Southeast New Mexico, Roswell.

Foley, Mary Helen Cleve and Melvin. Personal interview by Elvis E. Fleming, October 23, 1997.

Hinkle, James F. (Governor). Papers, Manuscript Collection No. 182, Rio Grande Historical Collections, New Mexico State University, Las Cruces.

Lincoln County Record of Marriage Certificates, Lincoln County Courthouse, Carrizozo, N. M.

Martínez, Cindy, Archival Assistant, Lincoln County Historical Society. Letter to Elvis E. Fleming, January 16, 1996.

Mathews, Dora M. *Petition to the Honorable Probate Court of Chaves County, Territory of New Mexico,* n.d. (1904). Chaves County Courthouse, Roswell, N. M.

McCombs, Joanne. Personal interviews by Elvis E. Fleming, September 27, 1995; October 7, 1997. Audio-tape Recordings, Archives, Historical Center for Southeast New Mexico, Roswell.

National Archives, Washington, D. C. "J. B. Mathis," Company M, 5th Regiment Tennessee Cavalry (USA), *Volunteer Enlistment; Declaration of Recruit; Consent in Case of Minor,* October 19, 1863; *Company Descriptive Book; Muster and Descriptive Roll of a Detachment of U. S. Vols. forwarded,* May 31, 1864; *Detachment Muster-in Roll,* May 31, 1864; *Company Muster Roll,* December 31, 1863, to April 30, 1864; *Company Muster Roll,* May and June 1864; *Company Muster Roll,* July and August 1864; *Company Muster Roll,* September and October 1864; *Company Muster Roll,* November and December 1864; *Returns,* January 26, 1865, *Company Muster Roll,* January and February 1865; *Company Muster Roll,* March and April 1865; *Company Muster Roll,* May and June 1865; *Company Muster-out Roll,* August 14, 1865.

National Archives, Washington, D. C. "Walter Mathis," Company H, 23rd Regiment Tennessee Infantry (CSA), Company Muster-in Roll, August 23, 1861; *Company Muster Roll,* January 1, 1862; *Register of Payments to Discharged Soldiers,* January 10, 1862.

Neuenschwander, Jan Armstrong. Personal interview by Elvis E. Fleming, October 7, 1997. Audio-tape recording, Archives, Historical Center for Southeast New Mexico, Roswell.

Park, Joan, Lincoln County Treasurer, Carrizozo. Letter to Elvis. E. Fleming, March 21, 1996.

Powell, H. J. Personal interview by Elvis E. Fleming, January 10, 1998.

Roswell Daily Record, various issues, June 4, 1904, through October 12, 1952.

Roswell Record, various issues, October 1, 1897, through June 10, 1904.

Roswell Register, various issues, February 27, 1897, through June 10, 1904.

Rudisill, Richard, Curator of Photographic History, Museum of New Mexico, Santa Fe. Letter to Elvis E. Fleming, December 18, 1995.

Ruidoso News, October 9, 1995.

Runyan, T. Edsil. Personal interview by Elvis E. Fleming, October 23, 1997.

Townsend, David. Letter to Elvis E. Fleming, September 1, 1997.

U. S. Bureau of the Census. *Seventh Census of the United States, 1 8 5 0 : Population.* Cannon County, Tennessee, p. 405, Household #756.

Von Bosse, Hennig. "Autobiography." MS, 1993. Archives, Historical Center for Southeast New Mexico, Roswell.

White, Jim, Postmaster, Farmington, N. M. Personal interview by Elvis E. Fleming, August 21, 1997.

Wilson, John P. Letter to Elvis E. Fleming, January 9, 1996.

Secondary Sources

An Illustrated History of New Mexico. Chicago: The Lewis Publishing Co., 1895.

Bidal, Lillian. *A Narrow Rugged Path: A Biography of Angie Lydia Hendrix Cleve.* Albuquerque: By the Author, 1995.

Bidal, Lillian. *Pisacah: A Place of Plenty.* El Paso: Robert E. and Evelyn McKee Foundation, 1996.

Bonney, Cecil. *Looking Over My Shoulder: Seventy-five Years in the Pecos Valley.* Roswell: By the Author, 1971.

Dillon, James A., Jr., McMinnville, Tennessee. "5th Tennessee Cavalry Regiment (USA) (Stokes)," MS, September 12, 1994. Archives, Historical Center for Southeast New Mexico, Roswell.

Fulton, Maurice Garland. *History of the Lincoln County War.* Tucson: University of Arizona Press, 1968.

Hinkle, James F. *Early Days of a Cowboy on the Pecos.* Roswell: F i r s t National Bank of Roswell, n.d.

Jacobsen, Joel. *Such Men as Billy the Kid: The Lincoln County War Reconsidered.* Lincoln, Nebraska: University of Nebraska Press, 1994.

Keleher, William A. *Violence in Lincoln County 1869-1881.* Albuquerque: University of New Mexico Press, 1957.

Lavash, Donald R. *Sheriff William Brady: Tragic Hero of The Lincoln County War.* Santa Fe: Sunstone Press, 1986.

Mathews, Ernest H. "Early Years in the Pecos Valley," in James D. Shinkle, *Reminiscences of Roswell Pioneers.* Roswell: By the Author, 1966.

Matloff, Maurice (ed.). *American Military History.* Washington: Office of the Chief of Military History, United States Army, 1969.

Nolan, Frederick. *The Lincoln County War: A Documentary History.* Norman: University of Oklahoma Press, 1992.

Pritchard, Stu. *Recuerdos de Ante Años.* Roswell: Roswell Savings & Loan Association, 1971.

Roswell Lodge, No. 18, Ancient, Free and Accepted Masons. Temple Book. Roswell: Roswell Lodge No. 18, 1914.

Tennesseans in the Civil War. 2 Vols. Nashville: Civil War Centennial Commission, 1965.

Utley, Robert M. *Billy the Kid: A Short and Violent Life.* Lincoln, Nebraska: University of Nebraska Press, 1989.

Waltrip, Lela and Rufus. *Artesia: Heart of the Pecos.* Canyon, Texas: Staked Plains Press, 1979.

Williams, Ernestine Chesser. "Buck Powell of the Río Peñasco," in *Treasures of History II: Chaves County Vignettes.* Roswell: Chaves County Historical Society, 1991.

Williams, Ernestine Chesser. *Echoes Break the Silence: A Collection of Articles from New Mexico and Arkansas.* Roswell: By the Author, 1987.

Wilson, John P. *Merchants, Guns & Money: The Story of Lincoln County and Its Wars.* Santa Fe: Museum of New Mexico Press, 1987.

98

Index